ARRL's
VHF DIGITAL
HANDBOOK

Steve Ford, WB8IMY

Production:
Jodi Morin, KA1JPA
Michelle Bloom, WB1ENT

Cover Design:
Sue Fagan, KB1OKW

Proofreader: Kathy Ford

First Edition

CONTENTS

Foreword

Acknowledgements

Index

FOREWORD

When the Internet became part of everyday life, the amateur packet radio networks that had flourished in the 1980s and early '90s declined sharply. To some, the collapse of packet spelled the end of digital Amateur Radio above 50 MHz. How wrong they were!

Although packet networks see less activity than they did decades ago, packet radio itself is far from dead. Packet radio has been "repurposed" to create the popular Automatic Position Reporting System, and traditional packet networks still exist to support public service activities. New software applications have greatly enhanced their function.

Thanks to pioneering work by Joe Taylor, K1JT, hams can now enjoy digital meteor scatter contacts and even moonbounce on VHF and UHF frequencies with modest stations. His *WSJT* software is available free of charge and requires little more than an ordinary computer sound device.

The Japan Amateur Radio League developed the D-STAR digital voice and data standard, and it has seen significant growth in the United States as hams establish D-STAR repeater networks on VHF, UHF and microwave bands.

Amateurs are even experimenting with the APCO-25 standard used by public service agencies. They're reprogramming commercial APCO-25 transceivers for use on 2 meters and 70 cm.

All of these topics, and more, are discussed in this edition of the *ARRL VHF Digital Handbook*. My hope is that you'll use this book not only as a helpful reference, but also as an inspiration to try your own VHF+ digital experimentation.

David Sumner, K1ZZ
Executive Vice President
Newington, Connecticut
January 2008

ACKNOWLEDGEMENTS

The author wishes to thank the following individuals and organizations, whose contributions helped make this book a reference that many readers will enjoy.

■ Allan Crosswell, N2YGK and Bill Covey, W1GTT, for their contributions to Chapter 2.

■ Rick Muething, KN6KB, Alan Isaachsen, KB2WF and Jim Oberhofer, KN6PE, for materials used in Chapter 3.

■ Ray Novak, N9JA, of ICOM America and Ward Silver, NØAX, for their contributions to Chapter 4.

■ Joe Taylor, K1JT, for his *WSJT Users Guide and Reference Manual,* portions of which appear in Chapter 5.

■ Pete Lunness, AScT, Training and Special Projects, Daniels Electronics Ltd, for the use of *Chapter 4: Anatomy Of The Common Air Interface* from the Daniels Electronics APCO-25 training manual, which has been reprinted in Appendix C.

■ T.J. Molenkamp, KC8LTS, for his contributions to Chapter 6.

■ John Champa, K8OCL, for authoring Chapter 7.

PACKET RADIO FUNDAMENTALS

*P*acket radio is not a new phenomenon. Nor is it confined to Amateur Radio, or to VHF, for that matter.

In the beginning, there was *X.25*, a protocol for wide-area digital networks that typically communicated over telephone lines. Without going into gory detail, X.25 works by chopping data into strictly defined *packets*, or *frames* of information. This is accomplished by a device known as a *Packet Assembler/Dissembler* or *PAD*. Each packet is sent to the destination device where another PAD checks it for errors. If errors are discovered, the packet must be sent again. This ensures that the data the user receives is 100% error free.

In the early 1980s, amateurs began adapting X.25 for over-the-air digital communications. The result was *AX.25*. The new AX.25 protocol worked in much the same way, although it identified each message by sender and destination station call signs and added a Secondary Station ID number (SSID) in a range from 0 through 15. The entire AX.25 protocol description is included as an appendix to this book.

As with X.25, each AX.25 frame has a defined structure as shown in **Figure 1-1**. The frame is logically broken up into the following fields:

Flag — The flag is a delimiter between frames. The 01111110 pattern is unique due to bit-stuffing (any time five 1s are seen, a zero is stuffed and vice-versa for decoding). Extra flags are permitted between frames. This gives receiver time to sync up to the received signal and also allows the transmitter to run continuously if it has to.

Address list — The address list is between 14 and 70 octets (2 and 10 call signs) and consists of a destination, source and up to 8 intermediate repeating stations. The address is 7 octets consisting of the call sign followed by the 4-bit (SSID) and 4 flag bits. Flag bits of note include the *repeated* and *end of list* (last repeating station) markers.

Control — This is used mostly for AX.25 connection-oriented protocol.

PID — The protocol ID identifies what higher-level protocol the frame carries data for. Examples include:

- AX.25 layer 3 (virtual circuits – connections)
- Internet Protocol (IP frames inside UI frames)
- Address Resolution Protocol (call sign-to-IP address)
- No layer 3 (UI frames)

Information — This is the "text" of the message.

FCS — A checksum used to detect garbled packets so they can be ignored.

Instead of a PAD to create and decode these AX.25 packets, hams invented the *Terminal Node Controller*, or *TNC*. Unlike PADs, TNCs do much more than assemble and disassemble data. A TNC is programmed to work within a radio network where there may be other competing signals. For example, to maximize the throughput for everyone on the same frequency, a TNC is designed to detect the presence of other data signals. If it has a packet to send, but detects a signal on the frequency, it will wait until the frequency is clear. TNCs also have a variety of user adjustments and other features, such as mailbox functions that allow them to store messages when the operators are away.

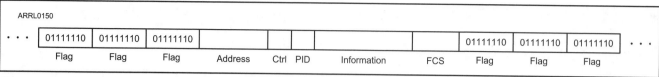

· · ·	01111110	01111110	01111110							01111110	01111110	01111110	· · ·
	Flag	Flag	Flag	Address	Ctrl	PID	Information	FCS		Flag	Flag	Flag	

Figure 1-1—The AX.25 packet frame structure (see text).

The First TNCs and the Packet Revolution

In March 1980 the Federal Communications Commission approved the use of the *American Standard Code for Information Interchange*, or *ASCII*, for Amateur Radio. Prior to 1980, hams had been restricted to the limited *Baudot* code familiar to radioteletype enthusiasts. Baudot can communicate the English alphabet, the number 0 to 9 and some punctuation. ASCII, in contrast, contains 128 letters, numerals, symbols and special codes, each of which is represented by a unique binary number. Every keyboard character is represented in this set. With ASCII, hams finally had access to what was then the standard language for computer-to-computer communication.

The FCC approval came 18 months after Canadian hams had been authorized to transmit ASCII and they had already been working on a protocol for doing so. To that end, Doug Lockhart, VE7APU, of Vancouver, British Columbia, developed the first TNC. It worked with a modem to convert ASCII to modulated tones and convert the demodulated tones back to ASCII. Doug had also formed the Vancouver Amateur Digital Communications Group (VADCG) and named his TNC the "VADCG board".

Hams in the US started experimenting with the VADCG board, but in December 1980 Hank Magnuski, KA6M, put a digital repeater on 2 meters using a TNC of his own design. A group of hams interested in Hank's TNC started working together on further developments in packet radio and formed the Pacific Packet Radio Society (PPRS). At the same time, AMRAD, the Amateur Radio Research and Development Corporation, in Washington, DC became the center for packet work on the east coast. In 1981 a group of hams in Tucson, Arizona, founded the Tucson Amateur Packet Radio Corporation (TAPR). With three centers of amateur packet research in the US, it wasn't long before one group would take the lead: TAPR.

TAPR pioneered the TNC-1, first commercially successful packet TNC in the United States. By 1984 they introduced its successor, the TNC-2. The TNC-2 design was much more compact, easy to use and highly reliable. The TNC-2 was enthusiastically received by the mushrooming amateur packet community, so much so that TAPR had difficulty keeping pace

with the demand. Soon after, several US manufacturers began producing their own TNCs based on the TAPR TNC-2 standard. In fact, the TNC-2 became *the* standard for packet radio world wide.

The packet fever spread quickly. For the first time, hams discovered that they could use ordinary VHF FM transceivers to create over-the-air data networks. These networks began springing up around the country, most centered on collections of stations that functioned as Packet Bulletin Board Systems, or *PBBSs*. Hams could connect to PBBSs directly, or through relaying stations, and read or send Amateur Radio e-mail. Some PBBSs offered small file downloads, too. It was even possible to configure your TNC mailbox function to automatically respond to queries from the PBBS and transfer e-mail without you ever lifting a finger.

Most user activity was conducted at a signaling rate of 1200 baud, although there were PBBSs that accepted 9600 baud connections. On the HF bands, hams are limited to 300 baud, but that didn't stop amateurs from setting up HF links to relay information between scattered packet networks throughout the nation and, eventually, the world. (Beware of confusing baud with bits per second. See the sidebar "Baud vs BPS vs Throughput.")

The TAPR TNC-2.

Then Came the Internet

The Internet had existed for years and was well known in government, military and academic circles. Its exposure to the general public in the late 1980s coincided with the increasing popularity of personal computers. Ordinary citizens began tapping the Internet through connections provided by their employers, or by colleges and universities. The revolutionary potential of the Internet was obvious, but unless you knew your way around the cryptic TCP/IP language, using the Internet could be a challenge. Something more was needed before the Internet could spread to an even larger audience.

"Something more" arrived in 1991. That was the year the Conseil Européen pour la Recherche Nucléaire (CERN) established their new World Wide Web project with Web "pages" created in *Hypertext Markup Language*, or *HTML*. In 1993 the National Center for Supercomputing Applications at the University of Illinois released *Mosaic*, the first Web browser. Finally, the public had an extremely "friendly" tool for navigating in cyberspace. The Web, as we know it today, was born.

The rest, as they say, is history. The Web exploded in popularity and within 5 years became mainstream technology, as familiar as a household telephone. Internet e-mail quickly became the standard for text communication with millions (and eventually billions) of people exchanging messages every day. What was once esoteric was now commonplace.

The effect of the Internet on packet radio was devastating. Unlike amateur packet radio, the Internet was extremely fast, reliable over long distances and capable of easily handling large file transfers. The allure of "instant" global e-mail was too great for most packet users to resist. They abandoned traditional packet radio in droves, which resulted in the shrinkage or collapse of amateur networks throughout the world. The effect was similar to the impact cellular telephones had on amateur repeater autopatch systems. Once everyone had an affordable and private wireless telephone, the practice of making a call through an autopatch was rendered obsolete.

This is not to say that amateur packet radio is dead. There are many packet networks still in place. What has happened instead is that packet radio has become *specialized* through applications designed to meet specific needs. We'll discuss these applications later in the book. The most popular application of AX.25 packet radio today is the Automatic Position Reporting System, or APRS, and that subject has a chapter all its own.

Baud vs BPS vs Throughput

These three terms are often confused and many hams use them interchangeably. By definition, however, they are quite different.

The *baud rate* is a measure of how many times per second a signal changes states (from "mark" to "space" in a radioteletype transmission, for example) in one second. The term "baud" comes from Emile Baudot, the inventor of the asynchronous telegraph printer.

BPS—Bits per Second—is a measure of how many bits per second are transmitted. With some digital coding schemes, it is possible to encode multiple bits per baud resulting in bit rates that exceed the baud rate.

Throughput is a measure of the amount of data transferred in a specific amount of time, usually expressed in bits per second (bps). This is a critical distinction because throughput can be independent of baud rate or encoded bits per second.

All three terms can come together in some interesting ways. Imagine you have a radio modem that creates a 1200 baud output signal. Thanks to clever coding, the modem is capable of encoding two bits for every signal change, so it is operating at 2400 bps (1200 baud × 2). So far so good, but let's say the radio is sending the 2400 bps data on a path that is prone to interference. The receiving station often detects errors and frames have to be re-transmitted many times. Even though the sending station is pumping data at 2400 bps, the throughput, based on the amount of data successfully decoded at the receiving station, is much lower.

Be wary when you read manufacturer claims about equipment that can transfer data at specific rates over radio channels. Do they mean the encoded bits per second at the transmitter, or the effective throughput? In most instances, they mean the data rate at the transmitter. When you take their hardware into the real world, your effective throughput may be dramatically different.

THE TNC: STILL AT THE HEART OF PACKET RADIO

Regardless of the changes in packet radio, the TNC is still a vital component. In essence, a TNC functions as a "radio modem." It acts the middleman between your radio and your computer. The TNC takes data from your computer, creates AX.25 packets and then transforms the AX.25 formatted data into audio signals for transmission by the radio. Working in reverse, the TNC demodulates the received audio, changes it back into data, disassembles the AX.25 packets and sends the result to the computer.

For 300 and 1200-baud applications, TNCs create signals for transmission using audio frequency shift keying (AFSK). Twelve hundred baud packet is most common and is used primarily at VHF. When creating a 1200-baud signal, a *mark* or 1 bit is represented by a frequency of 1200 Hz. A *space* or 0 bit is represented by a frequency of 2200 Hz. The transition between each successive mark or space waveform happens at a rate of 1200 baud. The frequencies of 1200 and 2200 Hz fit within the standard narrowband FM audio passband used for voice, so AFSK is accomplished by simply generating 1200 and 2200 Hz tones and feeding them into the microphone input of a standard FM voice transmitter.

Pure frequency shift keying is used for 9600 baud packet and this signal must be applied to dedicated 9600-baud ports on the transceiver.

A block diagram of a typical TNC is shown in **Figure 1-2**. You'll note that it has a serial interface connecting to a "terminal." The terminal can be a so-called "dumb terminal," which is little more than a keyboard and monitor screen. More commonly, the terminal is a full-fledged computer. Data flows to the computer and vice versa via this interface. At the heart of the TNC is the microprocessor and the attendant *High level Data Link Controller*, or *HDLC*. The microprocessor is the brain of the unit, but the HDLC is responsible for assembling and disassembling the packets. The modem is simply that—a modulator (changing data to audio tones) and demodulator (changing audio tones back to data).

You can still find TNCs for sale from manufacturers such as Timewave (**www.timewave.com**), MFJ (**www.mfjenterprises.com**) and Kantronics (**www.kantronics.com**). There are also several transceivers that have packet TNCs built in.

Talking to a TNC

The first step is to furnish the cable that connects the TNC to your computer at the COM port. In most cases this is an RS-232 serial cable. Most ham TNCs have yet to migrate to USB at the time of this writing.

Many TNC manufacturers supply software to communicate with the TNC, but any terminal program will work (Microsoft *Windows* includes such a program). You'll need to start that software and specify the COM port you'll be using, and set the baud and data parameters for that port. Refer to the manual for the specific program you've chosen. The baud rate of your computer must match the baud rate of your TNC. Some TNCs will automatically set their baud rate to match the computer. Other TNCs have software commands or switches for setting the baud rate. Again, you'll need to refer to your manual for specific instructions. When setting the data parameters, 8-N-1 is normally used: 8 data bits, no parity, and 1 stop bit. But like the baud rate, the computer and TNC parameters must match.

Once you have your communications program or packet software up and running, you need to set up your TNC. When you switch on the TNC, you should see some sort of "greeting" text on your screen. That's the first sign that all is well. If you see a bunch of gibberish, it means that the parameters of the TNC and computer don't agree and you'll have to make adjustments.

Now try sending a CONTROL-C to put the TNC into the *command mode* (the mode it needs to be in to accept commands from you). Press the **CNTRL** key and hold it down while tapping the **C** key. The TNC should respond with…

cmd:

This means that it is in the command mode and awaiting input from you. The first thing to do is put your call sign in the TNC's memory. Type MYCALL, your call sign and hit the **ENTER** key. Like this…

cmd: MYCALL WB8IMY

If you type MYCALL again and hit **ENTER**, the TNC should respond with your call sign. If so, the computer-to-TNC link is working fine. If you do not see anything on the screen when you type, enter the following:

cmd: ECHO ON

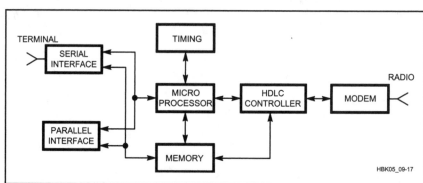

Figure 1-2—A functional block diagram of a typical packet radio TNC.

The Timewave PK-96 is a packet TNC capable of 1200 and 9600-baud operation.

If you see two of everything that you type, such as MMYYCCAALLLL, enter:

cmd: ECHO OFF

The next step is to open your TNC to communications with the world. Enter the following commands:

cmd:MONITOR ON <ENTER>

cmd: MRPT ON <ENTER>

TNCs and Radios

Twelve hundred baud packet tones can be fed directly into the microphone input of any VHF FM voice transceiver. To connect the radio and TNC, you will need to either purchase a custom-made cable, or build your own.

If you opt to craft your own cable, check your transceiver manual for the wiring diagram of the microphone jack. In most cases, there are separate connections for the audio input and the push-to-talk (PTT) line. (The TNC grounds the PTT line to key your transceiver.) Some transceivers also make receive audio available at the microphone jack for use with speaker/microphone combos. You can use this line to feed audio to the TNC. If it isn't available, you will have to make a separate connection to the transceiver's external speaker jack. **See Figure 1-3**.

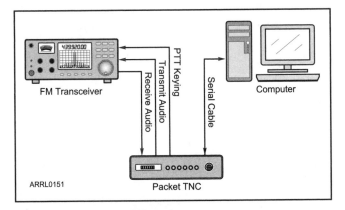

Figure 1-3—An outboard TNC connects to the computer through an RS-232 serial cable, although some recent models use a USB connection. The connections to the transceiver are for transmit audio, receive audio and push-to-talk (PTT) keying.

When you are setting up your TNC, be careful about pumping too much transmit audio into the radio. This will create distorted signals that won't be decodable at the receiving station.

An easy way to check your transmitted signal is to use the TNC *calibrate* function. Get to the command mode (CONTROL-C) and enter…

cmd: CALIBRATE

Listen to your transmitted signal with another rig and raise the audio level from the TNC until the received volume seems to stop increasing. Now reduce the audio from the TNC until you can just hear a volume decrease in the receiver. Reduce it a bit more and you're done.

Some TNCs have an audio output adjustment pot on the board, some have an adjustment accessible through a hole in the side of the unit and some have two fixed output levels selectable with a jumper. If one of these does not work, you may have to open up the transceiver and find the mic gain control. If this is necessary, be sure you adjust the mic gain control and *not* the deviation control. The mic gain control is before the limiters and the deviation control is after the limiters.

TNC Timing

Timing can use as critical as audio—both for the radio and the network.

The TNC's TXDELAY parameter specifies the delay interval between the time the TNC keys your radio and the moment when it starts sending data. Normally 300-400 milliseconds is adequate, but some 2-meter rigs take a bit longer for the phase-locked loop to set after the keying line is triggered. If you seem to be having a problem being heard and your audio seems normal, go to the command mode and try increasing TXDELAY to 400-600 milliseconds.

When you're part of a busy network, packets and packet acknowledgements are flying back and forth at a furious rate. One way to keep interference to a minimum is to manipulate the RESP (Response Time) and DWAIT parameters in conjunction with PERSIST and SLOTTIME to allow staggered transmissions. See your TNC manual for a list of all of these commands.

RESP is the time delay between reception of a packet and transmission of an acknowledgement. DWAIT sets the delay between the time when activity is last heard on the channel and the moment your radio transmits. You should set values of RESP and DWAIT to the values recommended in your area (the person managing the local network or PBBS should be able to tell you). Your TNC probably accepts a value in "counts" rather than in milliseconds, so don't forget to convert by the proper value in order to arrive at the correct timing value in milliseconds. For example, if you have been asked to set DWAIT to 600 milliseconds and the units of DWAIT for your TNC are 10 milliseconds per count, then you would command DWAIT = 60.

Most TNCs contain commands called PERSIST and SLOTTIME, which help enormously in avoiding interference. PERSIST sets the probability that a packet will be transmitted during a given time interval called a SLOTTIME. The parameter SLOTTIME governs the interval between transmission timing "slots." Initially, PERSIST should be set to approximately 64 and SLOTTIME to a value of about 10, which is equivalent to 100 milliseconds. PERSIST is the probability that when your TNC needs to transmit, it will transmit in the next time slot — if it doesn't transmit on this one, then, one slottime later, the same probability is applied. Eventually, the packet is transmitted, but the delay varies. This gives everyone a reasonable chance to get their data through.

FRACK (frame acknowledgement) should be set to 6 and RETRY to 10. FRACK sets the number of seconds between retries and RETRY sets the number of times your TNC will try to send a packet and gain acknowledgement of it before it gives up and disconnects

Monitoring

A little packet eavesdropping is the best way to get the scoop on what is going on in your area. With the radio cable connected, turn on your radio and increase the receiver volume to about the 10 o'clock position. Some TNCs include an LED indicator that shows that the TNC is receiving audio. Turn up the squelch control on the radio until the LED is extinguished. Tune the rig to any odd numbered frequency between 144.91 and 145.09, or between 145.61 and 145.79 MHz, and set the rig for simplex operation. With the decline in packet messaging networks, your best bet may be to search for a DX Packetcluster, or try monitoring Automatic Position Reporting System activity on 144.39 MHz. When you hear the buzzing packet signals and see text on your screen, you'll know you've hit the jackpot.

Depending on the type of activity you are monitoring, you may see what appears to be nonsense. If you are monitoring APRS, you'll see strings of numbers. These are latitude/longitude position reports. On

Packetclusters, which we'll discuss later in this chapter, you'll see DX call signs and frequencies.

"Connected" vs "Unconnected"

When discussing TNCs and networks, it is important to understand the difference between connected and unconnected communication.

If you are simply monitoring local packet transmissions, your TNC is in an *unconnected* state. What you see is what you get. If a signal is garbled by noise or interference, you'll see nothing on your screen (unless you've enabled the PASSALL function, in which case you'll see gibberish). If you transmit an unconnected packet, the signal simply leaves your antenna destined for nowhere in particular. Some stations may decode it, some may not.

When your TNC is operating in a *connected* state, everything changes. When you are connected, your station is linked to another station in a "virtual" sense. In a connected state, every packet you send is intended specifically for the receiving station (even though others can see it).

When your TNC transmits a packet, it starts a countdown clock. If the clock reaches zero before your TNC receives an acknowledgement (known as an *ACK*) that the packet arrived without errors, it will send the same packet again. When the packet is finally acknowledged, the TNC will send the next packet. And so it goes, one packet after another. The operator at the other station may also be sending packets to you since this communication process can flow in both directions simultaneously.

The big advantage of the connected state is that it ensures that data is delivered error-free. One packet station

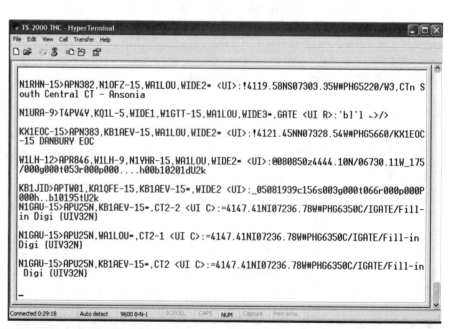

If you monitor 144.39 MHz with your radio and TNC, you may see Automatic Position Reporting System (APRS) traffic.

can connect to another directly, or through a series of relaying stations. Making a connection is easy. Just put the TNC in the command mode (remember **CNTRL-C**?) and enter the following…

cmd: Connect WB8IMY

(let's assume I have a packet station)

…or if you are using a relay station (N6ATQ in this example)…

cmd: Connect WB8IMY VIA N6ATQ

Your TNC will instantly begin sending a connect request. When my station receives your request, it confirms back to your TNC and a connected link is established. Depending on how you have your TNC software configured, you may hear a chime and see…

***CONNECTED TO WB8IMY

Now we're in the conversation or CONVERSE mode. Everything you type will be sent to me and vice versa. When we're finished with our error-free connected chat, do a CONTROL-C to get back into command mode on your TNC, or hit the **ESC** key if using the packet software,

then enter **D** to disconnect. You'll see "DISCONNECTED" on the screen.

While a connected state ensures error-free communication, its disadvantage is that it ensures error-free communication! At the risk of sounding very Zen about it, what benefits one situation can be a liability in another. Specifically, a connected state works best when signals are strong and interference is minimal. Remember that if too many packets are lost—by either not arriving at all or arriving with errors—the link will fail. That's why AX.25 packet radio tends not to work well on the HF bands. With all the noise, fading and interference, packets are often obliterated enroute.

Despite the advantages of being connected, there is something to be said for operating unconnected as well. Unconnected packets are ideal for applications where you are transmitting essentially the same information over and over. Since unconnected packets can be decoded by any station, they are an excellent means of disseminating non-critical data (data that doesn't need guaranteed error-free delivery) throughout a given area. If a station fails to decode one packet, it merely waits for the next one. The Automatic Position Reporting System uses exactly this approach.

What are the *Host* and *KISS* Modes?

You'll occasionally see references to packet radio TNCs functioning in "host mode" or KISS.

In simple terms, the TNC host mode is a bit of firmware inside the TNC that creates the interface between the TNC and the computer. The most popular host application was developed by Ron Raikes, WA8DED, and is found in many TNCs to this day. WA8DED's host provides two independent user interfaces. The default user interface is designed for use by a human operator at a terminal. The other mode is designed for TNC-to-computer communication where the TNC and specially developed packet software (the kind you might purchase from a vendor) communicate directly. The host mode creates a highly efficient environment for the TNC to "talk" with the application running on your computer. That's why most packet radio software vendors depend on the availability of a host mode in the TNC.

"KISS" stands for Keep It Simple, Stupid. The original idea started with Brian Lloyd, WB6RQN. Phil Karn, KA9Q, organized the specification and submitted an initial version in 1986. When a packet TNC is functioning in the KISS mode, the attached host computer has complete control of the TNC and the "conversation" between the TNC and the computer is strictly limited. In fact, the AX.25 protocol is removed entirely from the TNC, as are all command interpreters. Every inbound packet frame

is sent directly to the computer once it has been translated from HDLC to the asynchronous format the computer requires. The ultra-simplifed process works in the other direction as well. Asynchronous data frames from the host are sent to the TNC, but the TNC merely converts the frames to HDLC format and sends them to the radio for transmission.

When a TNC is running in KISS mode, it is up to the computer to do all the heavy lifting, so to speak. This is not a bad thing because it allows the software in the computer to do everything it needs to communicate with the outside world without the burden of engaging in an elaborate conversation with the TNC. There are several packet applications that use the KISS mode. The *AGWPE* software, which we'll discuss in the Winlink section in Chapter 3, uses the KISS mode.

The distinctions between the WA8DED host and KISS modes are transparent to the average packet user. The user's software places the TNC into the correct mode, and then returns it to normal operation when the software closes. There are times, however, when the open/close process goes awry and the TNC is left running in one mode or the other. Or, the TNC may not respond correctly when the user software commands it to enter KISS or the WA8DED host mode. Having at least a basic understanding or awareness of these modes will help streamline the troubleshooting process!

The Sound Card as TNC

Throughout this chapter we've discussed packet TNCs as outboard hardware devices. It is possible, however, to use your computer sound card (or sound chipset) as a TNC. The key to sound card packet is a free program called *AGWPE*. *AGWPE* was written by George Rossopoulos, SV2AGW. You can download it on the Web at **www.elcom.gr/sv2agw/inst.htm** (scroll down to "AGW Packet Engine"). *AGWPE* supports packet at 300, 1200 and 9600 baud.

With *AGWPE*, nearly all of the functions of the packet TNC take place within your computer, including the transmission and reception of packet signaling tones for your radio. The only outboard device you'll need is a simple sound card interface to such as those made by MFJ (**www.mfjenterprises.com**), TigerTronics (**www.tigertronics. com**), West Mountain Radio (**www. westmountainradio.com**) and many others. See the advertising pages of *QST* magazine. Figure 1A shows a typical interface installation. Note that in this example the interface is using a serial (COM) port, but you'll find USB interfaces as well.

AGWPE can work quite well and it is certainly an economical alternative to a stand-alone packet TNC. Much depends on audio settings and the compatibility of your sound card, though. Ralph Milnes, KC2RLM, has an excellent Web site devoted to *AGWPE*. You'll find it at **patmedia.net/ralphmilnes/ soundcardpacket/**.

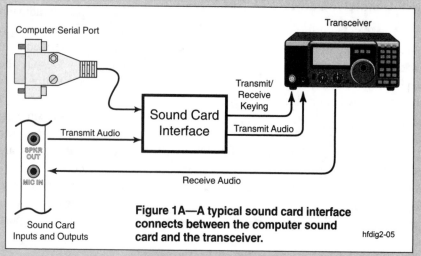

Figure 1A—A typical sound card interface connects between the computer sound card and the transceiver.

hfdig2-05

PACKET NETWORKS

The first packet networks were built on *digipeaters*. Digipeaters are simple digital relaying stations, somewhat like FM voice repeaters. If you make a connect request like this...

cmd: C WB8IMY VIA WR1B

...you are asking the WR1B digipeater to retransmit your packets to WB8IMY. The digipeater will obediently comply because it "sees" its call sign (WR1B) in the digipeater field of the packet frame.

This scheme works well when only a few people are on the radio channel. On crowded channels, however, a digipeater will quickly become overwhelmed and cause widespread interference. Worse yet, if the packet doesn't reach its destination through the digipeater, the origination station has to retransmit the entire packet again, causing even more congestion. See **Figure 1-4**.

NET/ROM and TheNet

NET/ROM and TheNet networking was introduced as a solution for the digipeater problem. Stations functioning in this configuration are more than simple relays, they are "intelligent" network *nodes* with the ability to route packets automatically without the user shouldering the burden of specifying and maintaining the circuit.

A user connects to a NET/ROM or TheNet node as if connecting to any other packet station. From there, he can issue commands to instruct the node to connect to another user locally, or connect to yet another node. As far as your TNC is concerned, it's only connected to the *first* node. Once a packet is successfully received by the first node, your TNC effectively "forgets" about it. It is now the responsibility of the node to pass the packet to the receiving station, or to another node. This reduces channel congestion and greatly increases reliability. See **Figure 1-5**.

NET/ROM and TheNet nodes don't use all of the AX.25 protocol. Instead, they use special AX.25 packets called *Unnumbered Information (UI)* packets, and then they place their own special protocol on top of AX.25. NET/ROM and TheNet nodes, at regular intervals, transmit to other nodes their current list of known nodes. In this way, each node is "aware" of the state of the network (which nodes are available and which ones are not). As new nodes come on-line, they are automatically integrated in the network, but there is a weakness in this approach. If there is a band opening, ordinarily unreachable nodes can suddenly find their way into the node lists. The same is true if a nearby node comes on the air briefly, but then leaves for whatever reason. The routing software doesn't know

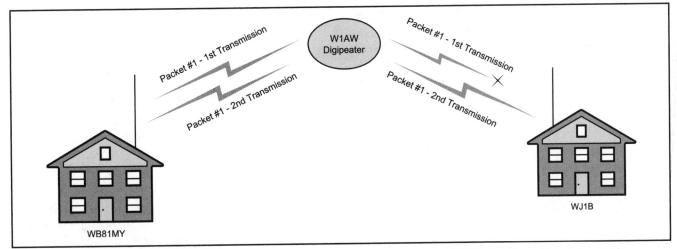

Figure 1-4—In this example, station WB8IMY sends each packet to WJ1B through the W1AW digipeater. The digipeater is functioning only as a relay. If the packet does not arrive intact at WJ1B, WB8IMY's TNC must send the entire packet again.

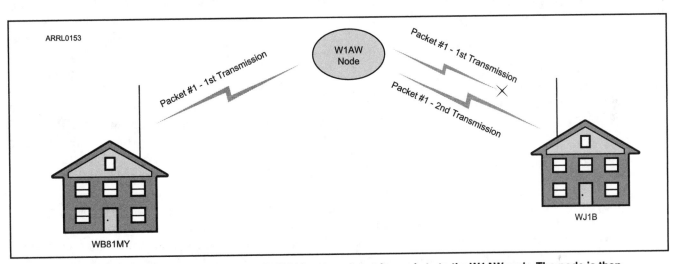

Figure 1-5—Packet nodes are intelligent relays. WB8IMY has to only get its packets to the W1AW node. The node is then responsible for getting the packets to WJ1B. If a packet is received with errors at WJ1B, the node re-sends the packet, not WB8IMY.

that these nodes are no longer reachable, but it tries anyway. The result is delayed or lost data.

ROSE

ROSE is another networking protocol derived from AX.25. Each ROSE node has a static (unchanging) list of the nodes it can reach. For a user to use a ROSE switch, he issues a connect with the destination station and in the digipeater field places the call of the local ROSE switch and the distant ROSE switch the destination station can hear. Other than that, the network is completely transparent to the user.

ROSE's use of static routing tables ensures that ROSE nodes don't attempt to route packets through links that aren't reliably reachable, as NET/ROM and TheNet nodes often do. However, ROSE suffers from the inability to automatically update its routing tables as new nodes come on-line.

The operators must manually update the routing tables, which is why ROSE networks require more maintenance.

TexNet

TexNet is a 3-port switch designed to create a 9600 baud backbone with 2 local access channels. The TexNet network provides transparent network access to the user. The user simply accesses his/her local TexNet node and then either connects to a user at another node or accesses various system services. TexNet provides the stability of fixed routing, while allowing new nodes to be automatically brought into the network.

FlexNet

Originally developed in Germany, FlexNet is one of the most advanced AX.25 packet network systems in use today. On a FlexNet network, each FlexNet node uses regular polling of its linked neighbors to verify that these links are currently available for network routing. An *autorouter* at each FlexNet node exchanges network-wide routing data with its FlexNet node neighbors. Whenever link conditions change anywhere within the network, routing data is updated network wide very quickly.

FlexNet features include:

- Hop-to-hop recovery of lost/damaged frames
- Simple route specification
- Automatic adaptive routing
- Improved adaptive channel access
- Support for Demand Assigned Multiple Access (DAMA)

Connecting to a station through a FlexNet nodes is extremely simple, which is part of its attractiveness. For example, assuming that N6ATQ and I can both hear the K1ZZ node, I only need to send the command...

cmd: CONNECT N6ATQ VIA K1ZZ

In a different example, let's say that N6ATQ is much farther away and can only hear the N6BV node. The K1ZZ FlexNet node automatically takes care of the packet routing to N6ATQ. All you have to do is specify that the N6BV node is the final node.

cmd: CONNECT N6ATQ VIA K1ZZ N6BV

The K1ZZ node will pick up your request and, as it dissects the packet, will see your request for packet routing to N6ATQ through the N6BV node. Once again, the Flex-Net network will take care of routing the packets to and from the N6BV node. All this will be completely transparent to you.

But what if you don't know which node N6ATQ is monitoring? FlexNet has a solution. Connect to any Flex-Net node and send the "find" command...

F N6ATQ

If a node has logged activity from N6ATQ, it will report back to you.

DX Packetclusters

DX Packetcluster networks are a modern version of an old concept: the DX spotting network.

Hams who chase contacts for DX Century Club award credits don't always have time to sit in front of radios, waiting for long-sought DX stations to suddenly appear on the air. Instead, they often rely on their fellow amateurs to sound the alarm. Before the advent of computer networks, hams called each other on the telephone to announce that a "rare" DX station was accepting contacts at a particular frequency. When FM repeaters appeared on the scene, it wasn't uncommon to set up a system solely for DX alerts. Hams could simply monitor the repeater frequency while they busied themselves with other tasks. If someone discovered a desired DX station on the air, they would announce the fact on the repeater for everyone to hear.

Packet radio offered a completely new approach to this old idea, one that became popular almost overnight. It began in the late 1980s when Dick Newell, AK1A, created the *PacketCluster* software. At the time of this writing, it is still the most popular software for this application, although there are newer contenders such as *AR-Cluster, CC Cluster, CLX, DX Spider* and others.

Packetcluster software acts as an aggregator of information, accepting input from various sources, then making that data available to any user who is connected to the network. Most Packetcluster networks are built around groups ("clusters") of node stations, all of which are running Packetcluster software. These nodes share information with each other, so what is "known" to one node is known to all. This node sharing can take place via RF links, or

What is DAMA?

Demand Assigned Multiple Access is an alternative channel access method that is designed to overcome some of the problems in commonly used Carrier Sense Multiple Access (CSMA).

The problem with CSMA is that everything depends on TNCs being able to detect activity on the frequency. Activity detection, combined with flexible transmit timing, can only work well on lightly used frequencies. As the number of signals increases, interference is inevitable. The result is that packets collide and must be re-transmitted over and over. This situation is made even worse when there are stations that cannot be heard by the rest of the group. The other stations will transmit right on top of these signals because they cannot detect their presence.

DAMA takes a completely different approach. In a DAMA network, the node or PBBS acts as a traffic cop (a so-called "DAMA Master"). The Master polls every station connected to it and the DAMA-capable TNCs will not transmit until they are polled by the Master. This technique keeps interference to a minimum. It is effective even where two of the connected stations cannot hear each other since they won't transmit until told to do so.

Many FlexNet networks use DAMA, as do other types of packet networks. To be compatible, your TNC must be DAMA compliant. The good news that most TNCs include a DAMA mode, but check and make sure before you buy.

by the Internet. Node networks can link to each other, creating large Packetcluster systems that cover whole states and regions.

Joining a Packetcluster is easy. You simply connect to your nearest node using a standard packet TNC and a 2-meter FM transceiver. No special software is required other than what is necessary for your computer to "talk" to your TNC.

When you connect to a Packetcluster node for the first time, you'll probably be asked to register with the network. Usually this involves sending your name and location.

To enter your name, type **SET/NAME <name>**

SET/NAME Steve

To enter your location, type **SET/QTH <qth>**:

SET/QTH Wallingford, CT

To use the features which give the DX station heading and sunrise-sunset times, you need to enter your latitude and longitude using **SET/LOC[ation]**:

SET/LOC[ation] 37 23 N 121 15 W

To verify the information entered, type in **SHOW/STA[tion] <yourcall>**:

SHOW/STA[tion] WB8IMY

Once you are registered, you'll begin receiving DX announcements, known as *spots*, from other hams who are connected to the network (**Figure 1-6**). To see the most recent spots, type **SHOW/DX.** to list the last five. If you're interested in one band, say 15 meters, type **SHOW/DX 15**. To list spots for a particular call, type **SHOW/DX <call>**:

SHOW/DX BS7H

If you're the lucky person who stumbles across a DX station, you can post a spot of your own. The format is: **DX <freq> <call> [optional comment]**:

DX 14223.4 PZ5RV

or...

DX 28012.0 9X5AA up 3 QSL via W4FRU

Spot Filtering

One of the nice features about Packetclusters is that you can configure your local node to only send the spots you want to see.

DX filtering is done by band, mode and DXCC entity. The general syntax of the filter command is:

SET/FILTER/mode/band=(x,x,x) DXCC-prefix(es)

Let's say that you don't want to see spots for stations in the United Kingdom, Spain, France and Germany on 10, 15 and 20 meters.

SET/FILTER/BAND=(10,15,20) G,EA,F,DL or, alternatively,
SET/FILTER/CW/SSB/BAND=(10,15,20) G,EA,F,DL

If the mode is not specified in the command, it defaults to both CW and SSB.

Filter out all announcements for spots on the 6 and 2 meter bands:

SET/FILTER/BAND=(6,2) ALL

Filter out spots for British stations on all bands:

SET/FILTER/BANDS=(ALL) G

Remember that the prefix field is prefix, and not country, sensitive, so if you want no Japanese spots, you will have to specify JH, JH, JI, JK, JL, JM, JN, JO, JP etc.

If you look at the list of common Packetcluster commands shown in **Table 1-1**, you'll quickly realize that there are many more features you can use. For instance, you can exchange e-mail with anyone on the network, or even chat in real time (not unlike instant messaging on the Internet). You can view propagation bulletins from National Institute of Standards and Technology radio station WWV. You can even ask the Packetcluster to estimate the maximum usable frequency from your location to any part of the world.

You find a directory of Packetcluster nodes throughout the country on the Web at **www.dxcluster.info/dxnodes. htm.**

Networks and Transparency

In our discussion of packet networks, it is important to point out that most of the interaction between the network and the user (that's you) is transparent. In other words, you can use any of these networks with a simple packet radio TNC and an FM transceiver. The commands

```
Welcome to the K1TTT AR-Cluster node Telnet port!
Please enter your call:
Hello Steven (WB8IMY)
Welcome to the YCCC K1TTT AR-Cluster Node in Peru Ma.
Available in Way-WMA on 145.690 or via telnet to kittt.net
For more info see http://www.kittt.net or email kittt@arrl.net
WWV: SFI=83  A=4  K=2 NO STORMS ; NO STORMS 5/4/2007 18:00Z
Your last login was 4/17/2007 01:35:57
TIP: SH/FZONE... = SH/ZONE with spots formatted in the real-time format
New Mail:  Personal = 0   Bulletin = 18
119 nodes, 96 local / 1197 total users  Uptime 1 20:51
WB8IMY de K1TTT     04-May 1853Z  arc >
DX de IZ8FWN:    10140.0  OZ1RD        you call cq on my freq!!!!!!!! 1853Z I
DX de PA7WB:     14180.6  OX/NA1SA     5  7  down 3              OX 1854Z PA
  14180.6  OX/NA1SA     04-May-2007 1854Z  5  7  down 3          OX <PA7WB>
   7068.0  AO5KB        04-May-2007 1854Z                        EA <EC4DEP>
  10140.0  OZ1RD        04-May-2007 1853Z  you call cq on my freq!!!!!!!!<IZ8FWN>
  28500.0  JATEST       04-May-2007 1852Z  Test!!!!              JA <WD9IDV>
  18150.0  TI8II        04-May-2007 1852Z                        TI <W5TFW>
  14000.0  G6IQL        04-May-2007 1852Z  SPOON FED ALWAYS EASY! G <G4WFQ>
 144320.0  LA2PHA       04-May-2007 1852Z  52 jo38 jo42          LA <DK4U>
  14190.0  XU7TZG       04-May-2007 1851Z  5-10 up VERY easy!    XU <G6IQL>
  10140.9  DK0OF        04-May-2007 1851Z  CQ RTTY               DL <9A3GS>
  14195.0  BS7H         04-May-2007 1851Z  Was 'G' only=Easy/1'st call! <G6IQL>
WB8IMY de K1TTT     04-May 1853Z  arc >
DX de EW6BN:     10105.5  JA7ARM       CQ...                     JA 1854Z EU
```

Figure 1-6—Connecting to the K1TTT Packetcluster node and obtaining a list of the latest DX spots.

Table 1-1
Common Packetcluster Commands

Command	Syntax	Command Description
ANNOUNCE	A msg	Announcement to LOCAL users only
ANNOUNCE/nodecall	A/call msg	Announcement to users on node (call)
ANNOUNCE/FULL	A/F msg	Announcement to users on ALL NODES
BYE or QUIT	B or Q	Log off node
DELETE or KILL	DE msg# or K #	Delete a mail message
DIRECTORY or LIST	DI or L	List last 5 mail messages
DIRECTORY/ALL	DI/A	List all active mail messages
DIRECTORY/NEW	DI/N	List all new mail messages
DIRECTORY/OWN	DI/O	List mail TO or FROM you
DX	DX fq call cmt	Announce a DX station
HELP	H or ?	Brief command summary
KILL or DELETE	K msg# or DE #	Delete a mail message
LIST or DIRECTORY	L or DI	List last 5 mail messages
QUIT or BYE	Q or B	Log off node
READ	R	Read a mail message TO YOU
READ	R msg#	Read a specific mail message
READ	R/filearea fn	Read a file in a specified filearea
REPLY	REP	Reply to a read message TO YOU
REPLY/DELETE	REP/D	Reply to a read message & delete
SEND	S all or call	Send a mail message to (all) (call)
SEND/PRIVATE	S/P call	Send a PRIVATE mail message
SEND/RR	S/RR call	Send mail message with return receipt
SET/HERE	SET/H	Specify you're at the keyboard
SET/LOCATION	SET/LO	Enter your latitude/longitude
SET/NAME	SET/NA	Enter your name
SET/NEED	SET/NE pfx,pfx	Specify your needed countries
SET/NOHERE	SET/NOH	Specify you're away from keyboard
SET/NONEED	SET/NON pfx	Delete needed countries
SET/QTH	SET/Q	Enter your address/city
SHOW/ANNOUNCEMENT	SH/AN	Show last 5 TO ALL announcements
SHOW/BULLADDR	SH/BULLA	Show list of TO ALL mail addresses
SHOW/BULLETINS	SH/BU	Show files in BULLETIN files area
SHOW/CLUSTER	SH/CL	Show number of nodes & users
SHOW/COMMANDS	SH/COM	Show available DATABASE commands
SHOW/CONF/NODE	SH/C/N	Show nodes connected
SHOW/CONFIGURATION	SH/C	Show nodes and users connected
SHOW/DX	SH/D	Show last 5 DX announcements
SHOW/DX	SH/D band	Show last 5 DX spots on (band)
SHOW/DX	SH/D call	Show last 5 DX spots for (call)
SHOW/DX	SH/D frq1 frq2	Show DX spots between Freq1-Freq2
SHOW/FILES	SH/FI	Show files in GENERAL files area
SHOW/HEADING	SH/H prefix	Show beam heading to a country
SHOW/LOCATION	SH/LOC call	Show lat/long/distance for user
SHOW/LOG	SH/LOG	Show last 5 system log entries
SHOW/LOG	SH/LOG call	Show system log for user (call)
SHOW/MUF	SH/MU prefix	Show MUF to country (prefix)
SHOW/NEED	SH/NE call	Show country needs of user (call)
SHOW/NEED	SH/NE prefix	Show user calls needing (prefix)
SHOW/NOTICE	SH/NO	Show (review) local node notice
SHOW/PREFIX	SH/PR prefix	Show country assigned and zones
SHOW/STATION	SH/ST call	Show information on user (call)
SHOW/SUN	SH/SU prefix	Show sunrise/sunset for (prefix)
SHOW/USERS	SH/U	Show users logged onto local node
SHOW/USERS/FULL	SH/U/F	Show users logged onto all nodes
SHOW/USER	SH/U call	Show NAME/QTH of user (call)
SHOW/WWV	SH/W	Show last 5 WWV announcements
TALK	T call	Enter talk mode to a user (call)
TALK	T call msg	Send a 1-line message to user (call)
TYPE	TY fn.ext	Display a file in BULLETIN area
TYPE/FILES	TY/FI fn.ext	Display a file in GENERAL area
UPDATE	UPD/filename	Update a DATABASE file (restricted)
UPLOAD/BULLETIN	UPL/BU fn.ext	Upload a file to BULLETIN file area
UPLOAD/FILE	UPL/FI fn.ext	Upload a file to GENERAL file area
WWV	WWV sfi=,a=,k=	Send Solar Flux as reported on WWV
EXIT MESSAGE	/EXIT	Enter command on a new line to exit

you'll use to access the network may vary, but everything else remains the same. *You do not have to purchase special hardware or software to use any of the AX.25 networks discussed in this chapter.*

As I stated earlier, the best approach at first is to simply monitor local packet activity. By doing so you'll pick up clues about which types of networks are active in your area. Also try a Web search for more information about local packet activity. You may be able to find lists of networks and network maps.

PACKET BEYOND 1200 BAUD

Nearly all of the activity we've discussed so far involves 1200-baud packet. This is the defacto standard for AX.25 packet networks in the United States. Compared to even the slowest Internet dial-up access rates, 1200 baud is slow indeed!

There have been efforts to move the amateur packet community to 9600 baud and higher, but they've met with limited success. Ninety-six hundred baud activity occurs most often among network backbones where the additional speed is particularly helpful.

The reason that most users remain stuck at 1200 baud is because few FM transceivers can adequately handle 9600 baud signals. As I stated earlier, 1200-baud signaling tones can be easily applied to the microphone jack of any FM transceiver. This is *not* true for 9600-baud tones. They must be applied after the microphone amplifier stage to avoid distortion. This requires a separate, dedicated audio input. Manufacturers of FM base and mobile transceivers began offering 9600-baud inputs a number of years ago,

but the performance of many of these transceivers at 9600 baud is uneven at best.

Every transceiver that offers a 9600-baud input is tested when it is evaluated in *QST* magazine's "Product Review" column. Look for the BER (bit error rate) test results. Some transceivers can handle 9600 baud signals well, but others fall short.

Another issue is that there has not been a groundswell of user demand for 9600-baud-and-above access in amateur packet networks. Since most users are exchanging only text messages, they've found 1200 baud to be adequate. If you're satisfied with packet performance at 1200 baud, it is difficult to justify the expense of a 9600-baud-capable transceiver and a 9600-baud TNC. (Yes, your TNC must be capable of 9600 baud, too.)

Hams have been exploring other digital options for breaking through the 1200 baud ceiling. One of them is known as *D-STAR* and this book devotes an entire chapter to the topic.

AUTOMATIC POSITION REPORTING SYSTEM – APRS

The Automatic Position/Packet Reporting System, better known as *APRS*, was the brainchild of Bob Bruninga, WB4APR. In fact, APRS® is a trademark registered by WB4APR. The original application of APRS was to track moving objects, and that's still its primary use today. Even so, APRS can do much more such as short text messaging, telemetry and so on.

APRS stations transmit position information that is decoded at the receiving stations. Station positions are represented by symbols (called *icons*) on computer-generated maps. When a station moves and transmits a new position, the icon moves as well. When you click on the icon with your mouse cursor, you see information such as speed, direction of travel and more.

Any discussion of APRS must begin with the technology that lies at its heart: the *Global Positioning System*.

THE EVOLUTION OF GPS

The Global Positioning System (GPS) is a satellite-based radionavigation system that uses 24 orbiting satellites to provide a highly accurate position finding capability anywhere on the face of the Earth anytime, day or night. Although GPS has become the best known electronic navigation system today, it was not the first. GPS was preceded by other well known electronic navigational aids including radio direction finders (RDF), hyperbolic systems (OMEGA, DECCA. Loran-A, and Loran-C), and the very first satellite based navigational aid, TRANSIT.

The Global Positioning System is owned and managed by the US Department of Defense. The official name of the system is NAVSTAR, which is an acronym for **NAV**igation **S**atellite **T**iming and **R**anging. To meet US requirements for a highly accurate electronic navigational system for military and intelligence communities, the Department of Defense began research and development of GPS in 1973. The United States Air Force was named as the lead agency for this multiservice program. The first GPS satellite was launched on February 22, 1978.

GPS was originally developed strictly for military use. This changed in 1983 after the downing of Korean Air Flight 007 by the Soviet Union. This tragedy occurred in part because the crew of the Korean 747 aircraft made an error in navigation which brought the aircraft over Soviet air space. It was argued that if GPS had been available this tragedy would not have occurred. As a result, President Ronald Reagan issued an Executive Decree that certain portions of the GPS system be made available free of charge to the entire world. The US military insisted, however, that those portions of the GPS made available for civilian use be degraded in accuracy so that the system could not be used by the enemies of the US for clandestine purposes. When the Standard Positioning Service portion of the GPS was opened up to everyone, it came with something called Selective Availability (SA) which degraded the normal accuracy of 50 feet to 300 feet.

Even with portions of GPS now open to civilian use, there were very few GPS receivers available, and any to be found were very expensive. In 1991, during Operation

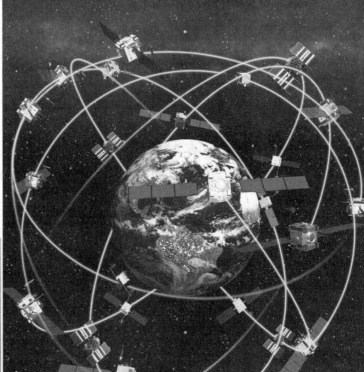

When this book was written, the GPS network was supported by 24 satellites orbiting the Earth.

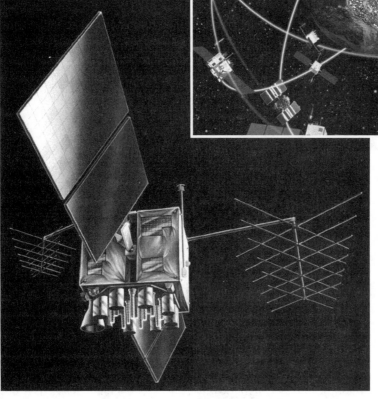

A typical GPS satellite.

A portable GPS receiver.

Desert Storm, the use of GPS was so widespread that the military found they did not have enough GPS receivers to supply the troops. A large multi-sourced procurement by the military for GPS receivers resulted in a tremendous spin-off of the technology into the civilian sector. This, in turn, resulted in the availability of highly capable GPS receiver equipment to the global market. Although GPS receivers were expensive at first, widespread acceptance of the technology and a flood of receiver equipment has resulted today in a basic unit that can give position location accuracy to within 10 feet and can be purchased for less than $100.

After many studies and considerable lobbying in

Congress, President Clinton ordered that SA be permanently turned off on May 2, 2000. The improvement in GPS accuracy for the civilian world since then has been considerable, and the military has found a way of locally degrading GPS accuracy for selected areas without affecting the rest of the system.

GPS and APRS

With the sudden availability of affordable GPS receivers, it wasn't long before WB4APR and others began experimenting with them. They discovered that it was possible to tap the GPS receiver's data stream and extract position information that could then be sent via amateur packet radio. At the receiving end, special software was used to decode the position information and create symbols on computer-generated maps. Whenever the GPS receiver moved, a new position report was transmitted. When the receiving station decoded the signal, it "moved" the map icon to the new position. APRS as we know it today was born!

Virtually all APRS activity takes place today on 144.39 MHz using 1200-baud packet TNCs and ordinary FM voice transceivers. In areas where the APRS network is particularly active, you may hear traffic on 445.925 MHz, and there is some activity on HF at 10.151 MHz (LSB).

SETTING UP AN APRS STATION

If you own a 2-meter FM voice transceiver, you already have the primary component of your APRS station. Tune your radio to 144.39 MHz and listen for packet transmissions. If you hear them, it means you have APRS activity in your area.

To decode APRS packets, you'll need a TNC—either an outboard hardware TNC, a radio with a built-in TNC or you can use a sound-card TNC with one of many soundcard interfaces that are available. See Chapter 1 for tips on buying and installing TNCs. The TNC doesn't necessarily have to be "APRS compatible." APRS compatibility is only a factor if you wish to connect the TNC to a GPS receiver, weather station or other data source.

Using the TNC **MYCALL** command, you can enter your call sign followed by your *SSID*, or *Secondary Station Identifier*, if you wish. (We discussed SSIDs in Chapter 1.) A typical SSID might be W1AW-*10*. An SSID is not required for APRS, although many APRS operators use them to distinguish between their home and mobile stations. For instance, WB8IMY is my home station, but WB8IMY-*5* is my APRS mobile station.

But do you really need a GPS receiver? Well…it depends. If all you want to do is monitor APRS activity, you do *not* need a GPS receiver. If you want to participate in the local APRS network from a fixed (non-moving)

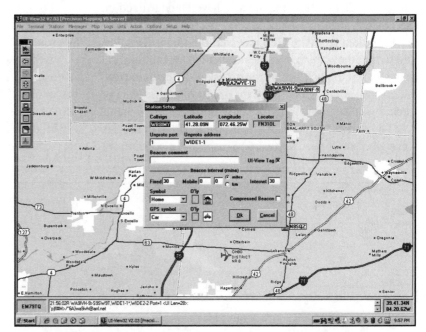

UI-View for *Windows* is available at **www.ui-view.org/**. This view shows a *UI-View* station setup screen. Note the unproto path statement and the fields for latitude and longitude.

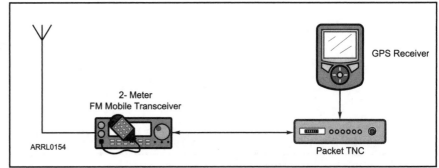

Figure 2-1—A typical mobile APRS station equipped with a packet TNC and a GPS receiver.

station such as your home, you still do not need a GPS receiver. Just determine your home latitude/longitude coordinates and you can use them to establish the location of your home station on the network. There are numerous sites on the Internet that will convert your home address to a correct latitude and longitude.

The only APRS station that requires a GPS receiver is a *moving* station. The good news is that almost any GPS receiver will do the job. It does not have to be elaborate or expensive. The only requirement of an APRS-compatible GPS receiver is that it provide data output in *NMEA* (National Marine Electronics) format. Beware, however. Many GPS receivers advertise the fact that they provide data output, but some do it in a proprietary format, not NMEA. Check carefully and make sure the data is available in standard NMEA format. See **Figure 2-1** for a diagram of a typical mobile APRS station with a GPS receiver.

The reason NMEA is important is that APRS-compatible TNCs and tracking devices have standardized on the NMEA protocol (specifically, NMEA 0183). They "expect" data from the GPS receiver to be in NMEA format so that they can extract the necessary information and massage it into packets for transmission. If the data from the GPS receiver is in a non-NMEA format, the TNC or tracker won't be able to make sense of it.

The critical component of a fixed APRS station is software. You'll need software to display the positions of APRS stations, along with other information contained in their transmissions. APRS software is also essential if you want to communicate over the APRS network. Note, however, that APRS software is *not* necessary for mobile stations that wish to merely transmit APRS beacons for tracking purposes. That function is carried out automatically using the GPS receiver and ARPS-compatible TNC or tracking device.

Since most amateurs use Microsoft *Windows* on their station computers, the most widely used APRS software is written for *Windows*. The most popular APRS *Windows* program by far is *UI-View. UI-View* was created by the late Roger Barker, G4IDE. You'll find it on the Web at **www.ui-view.org/**. The 16-bit version is free for downloading. To use the 32-bit registered version, hams are asked to donate to their local cancer charities. Details are available on the *UI-View* Web site.

Mac users aren't left out, though. Many use *MacAPRS* at **www.winaprs.org/MacAPRS.htm**.

For *Linux* there is *Xastir,* which is the most widely used *Linux* application for APRS. It is free for downloading at **www.xastir.org/**.

APRS software, regardless of the operating system, is designed to "talk" to the packet TNC, processing the incoming APRS data and creating icons on your computer screen. The application also uses the TNC to transmit APRS data. As we discussed in Chapter 1, this means that the software and the TNC must be communicating with each other at the same baud rate. Every APRS application has a setup menu that allows you to program the correct parameters to communicate with the TNC.

Depending on the software, there may be other features such as logging, messaging and more. Software changes rapidly, so it isn't practical to document the functions of every program in this book. Fortunately, most APRS applications come with "help" files that describe how to use the software. Others include full-featured manuals that are downloadable online.

Maps and APRS

No matter which APRS software you choose, one highly important aspect is the mapping function itself. To get the most from APRS, your software maps must be as comprehensive as possible, preferably with the ability to show detail down to street level.

Downloadable APRS software applications generally do not come with detailed maps. The reason is that detailed map files

In this view, the *UI-View* map is centered on an area south of Dayton, Ohio. You can see several mobile stations and a fixed (home) station.

Table 1
Partial List of APRS Symbols and Descriptions

A data string that makes up a standard APRS position report looks something like this:

!3612.34N/11518.95W>

The latitude and longitude are expressed in degrees, minutes and decimal fractions of minutes. This is the standard NMEA format for lat/long output by GPS receivers, and is also the default format for APRS. Thus, the example above says, "36 degrees 12.34 minutes north latitude" and "115 degrees 18.95 minutes west longitude". The character after the longitude, at the end of the string, specifies the symbol that will appear on monitor screen at the receiving stations. In this example, it would be a car.

Symbol	Description	Symbol	Description	Symbol	Description
!	Police or Sheriff	>	Car	]	WinLink PBBS (Mailbox)
#	Digipeater	?	File Server, Position Server	_	Weather Station
	(Green Hollow Star)	@?	Hurricane, Tropical Storm	a	Ambulance
$	Telephone	A	Aid Station	b	Bicycle
&	Gateway	C	Canoe	d	Fire Department
(	Cloudy	E	Eyeball	e	Horse
*	Snowmobile	G	Grid Square (6-Digit)	f	Fire Truck
+	Red Cross	H	Hotel (Blue Dot)	g	Glider, Hang Glider
,	Boy Scouts	I	TCP	h	Hospital
-	House, QTH with vertical	K	School	i	Islands On The Air (IOTA)
	antenna	M	MacAPRS	j	Jeep
0	Circle (Numbered)	N	NTS Station	k	Truck
1	Circle (Numbered)	O	Balloon	m	MIC-Encoder Repeater
2	Circle (Numbered)	P	Police Car	n	Node
3	Circle (Numbered)	R	Recreational Vehicle	o	Emergency Operations Center
4	Circle Numbered	S	Space Shuttle	p	Rover, Dog
5	Circle (Numbered)	T	SSTV	q	Grid Square (4 Digit)
6	Circle (Numbered)	U	Bus	r	Antenna
7	Circle (Numbered)	V	ATV	s	Power Boat
8	Circle (Numbered)	W	National Weather Service	t	Truck Stop
9	Circle (Numbered)	X	Helicopter	u	Truck, 18 Wheeler
:	Fire	Y	Yacht, Sailboat	v	Van
;	Campground, Tent, Portable	Z	WinAPRS	w	Water Station
<	Motorcycle	[	Runner, Jogger	x	X-APRS (UNIX APRS)
=	Railroad Engine	\	Triangle (Direction Finding)	y	House, QTH with Yagi Antenna

are numerous and large—it would not be practical to bundle these files with every APRS program. Instead, most applications are designed to import user-created custom maps, or to work with existing commercial mapping programs that are commonly available for sale on CDs or DVDs. Examples include Microsoft *Streets*, Delorme *Street Atlas* and Under-Tow's *Precision Mapping*.

UI-View, for example, has the ability to automatically load and display maps from *Precision Mapping*. You must purchase and install *Precision Mapping* on your PC, then download and install a small *Precision Mapping* "server" application into *UI-View*.

Each APRS transmission includes characters that define the type of map icon that will be displayed at the receiving end. A list is shown in **Table 2-1**. If

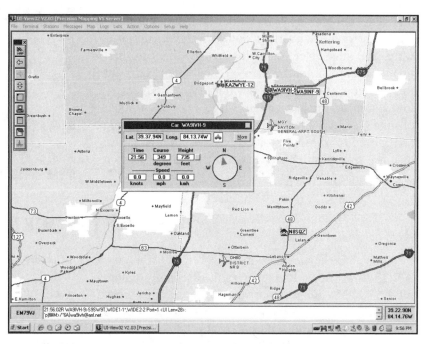

If you double click on an APRS icon in *UI-View*, a small window opens to display more detail about the station.

you are operating a fixed station, your APRS software will allow you to choose your icon (mine is a symbol in the shape of a house). If you are a mobile station using a traditional TNC, you'll need to define your chosen icon in your beacon statement. APRS-compatible TNCs give you the ability to do this. APRS trackers (which we'll discuss in a moment) also allow you to choose your icon when you program the unit. Your mobile icon might be a car, boat, airplane, etc.

APRS and "Real Time"

When you are viewing local APRS activity on your computer, keep in mind that the icons may not represent the true positions of stations in "real time." Obviously, buildings do not move, so you can be confident that those icons rep-resent station positions that are essentially unchanging.

Mobile icons are another matter. Every icon you see on your screen represents the *last reported position* of that particular station—or at least the position defined by the last packet transmission you decoded. If your computer displays an icon of a mobile station that's moving at 60 MPH down I-95 at exit 27, in reality that vehicle is probably some distance from where the icon shows it to be. There are several reasons for this. The vehicle only sends beacons at certain intervals, so a few minutes may have elapsed since the last transmission. It is also possible that the vehicle moved into a location where no digipeaters could receive and relay its transmissions, which means you didn't receive subsequent position reports. Finally, interference on the frequency may have blocked the vehicle packets from reaching your station.

APRS TRACKERS

You can create a mobile APRS station with a VHF FM transceiver, a TNC and a GPS receiver. Wire everything together, connect an antenna, supply dc power and you're set. For hams on the go, however, it's common to replace the full-fledged TNC with an APRS *tracker*. An APRS tracker is a compact device designed for one purpose: to receive data from the GPS receiver, assemble APRS packets from the data and create modulated signals for use by the transmitter. Some APRS trackers include GPS receivers in their designs. You'll even find trackers that are complete packages incorporating tiny GPS receivers and low power FM transmitters.

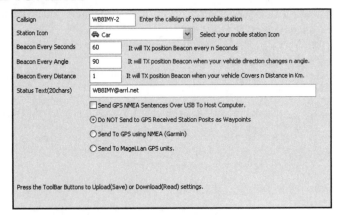

A typical tracker software setup screen.

To use a tracker you must program it the same way that you initially program a TNC. Like TNCs, trackers connect to computer serial ports for programming and most come with their own programming software. You must enter your call sign and other information such as your beacon interval (how often you want the tracker to transmit your position). Most trackers allow you to set the beacon interval to a certain amount of time (say, every two minutes). Some trackers can be configured to transmit position beacons after a certain distance (every mile), or whenever the vehicle turns a corner.

The popular TinyTrak3 takes the output from a GPS receiver and assembles packet signals for transmission. It is available at **byonics.com/tinytrak/**.

APRS NETWORKING

One of the key features of APRS is that while it uses AX.25 to transport its messages, it essentially ignores all the AX.25 connection-oriented baggage. This means unlike the packet operations described in the previous chapter, APRS stations do not establish "connections" with each other. Instead, APRS packets are sent to no one in particular, meaning to *everyone*.

Every APRS station has the ability to function as a digital repeater, or *digipeater*. So, if it receives a packet, it will retransmit the packet to others. As other digipeaters decode the same packet, they will also retransmit and spread it further. This is known as *flooding* and is illustrated in **Figure 2-2**.

As an APRS user, you can set up your station to address

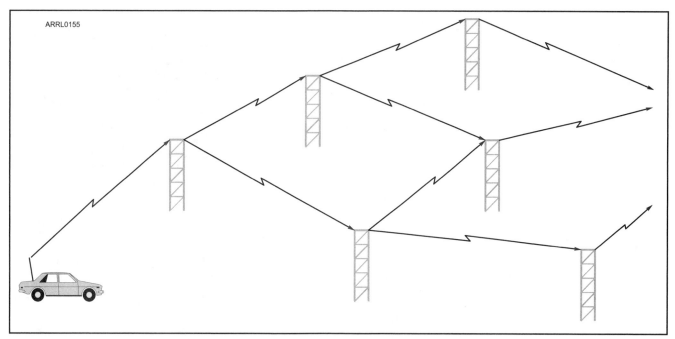

Figure 2-2—In this example, an APRS packet is transmitted by a mobile station and is retransmitted by a nearby digipeater. Depending on how the mobile operator configured his TNC or tracker's path statement, the packet will be picked up and repeated by several other digipeaters. This is known as flooding.

its packets through specific digipeaters according to their call signs. But when you're traveling, how do you determine which digipeaters you should use? This may sound like a difficult problem, but APRS has a built-in solution.

Paths and Aliases

If I was a criminal mastermind, news reporters might identify me like this:

Steve "The Cat" Ford

My true name is Steve Ford, but my *alias* in the crime world might be "The Cat." (Yes, I have a fondness for cats.) Steve Ford and "The Cat" are interchangeable; they both function as labels for the same person.

In the packet world, nodes and digipeaters can have aliases, too. My digipeater call sign may be WB8IMY-1, but I can also assign an alias, using the MYALIAS command in my digipeater TNC. Perhaps my digipeater alias would be WLFD (meaning my home town of Wallingford). You can route packets through my digipeater by addressing them to WB8IMY-1, or simply by addressing them to WLFD. Any station that is set up to respond to an alias is capable of handling your packets automatically, even if you don't know its call sign.

Unlike typical packet use of aliases, in which a given single station has a specific alias, APRS specifies standard digipeater aliases that nearly all stations use. This means that you can travel anywhere in the country and still participate in the APRS network without knowing digipeater call signs. (Otherwise, you'd have to reconfigure your TNC

whenever you moved from one area to another.) The most common APRS digipeater alias is *WIDEn-n*.

To address the increasing congestion on APRS networks, the WIDEn-n system was introduced in 1994 and by 2004 was in widespread use. The letter "n" represents a number. The first (left-most) "n" designates the type of WIDE digipeater that will relay your packets. A WIDE1 digipeater is a limited coverage "fill in" relay. A WIDE2 digipeater is for wide coverage. The second "n" is the Secondary Station Identifier (SSID) that we discussed earlier, as well as in Chapter 1. The digipeater's SSID is used in APRS networks as a means of limiting how often (and how far) a packet can be repeated.

Here's how it works. Each time your packet traverses a WIDEn-n digipeater, the digipeater subtracts 1 from the SSID as it retransmits. The next digipeater deducts 1 and so on until the SSID reaches zero, at which time the packet will not be repeated again. This has the effect of limiting the flood radius. See **Figure 2-3**.

When you configure a TNC or tracker for use with APRS, you can use these aliases to set up the paths for the beacon packets you'll be transmitting. In most devices this is accomplished with the UNPROTO parameter, sometimes simply referred to as the "Path." If you are a fixed station (a station at home, for instance), set your path as...

WIDE2-2

(or with a traditional TNC UNPROTO statement, set it to APRS VIA WIDE2-2).

This designates that your reports will be relayed by *two*

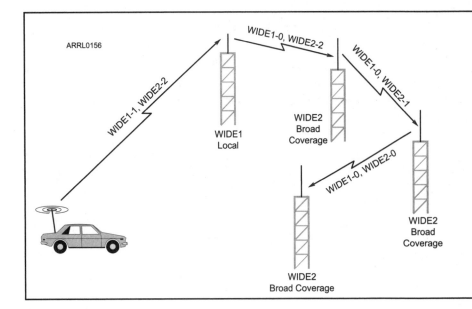

ARRL0156

WIDE1-1, WIDE2-2

WIDE1-0, WIDE2-2

WIDE1-0, WIDE2-1

WIDE1
Local

WIDE2
Broad
Coverage

WIDE1-0, WIDE2-0

WIDE2
Broad
Coverage

WIDE2
Broad Coverage

Figure 2-3—By using the WIDEn-n system, we can limit packet flooding in a local network and greatly reduce congestion. The mobile station in this example has his path set as WIDE1-1,WIDE2-2. Notice how his packet propagates through the network and how the SSID number is reduced by one each time the packet is repeated through a digipeater with a corresponding alias. When it leaves the WIDE1 digipeater, the WIDE1 SSID is set to zero. WIDE1 digipeaters will not relay this packet, but the WIDE2 digipeaters will. When it reaches the third WIDE2 digipeater, the counters all reach zero and digipeating stops.

WIDEn-n digipeaters (remember that a WIDE2 digipeater is a broad-coverage relay) and limits the spread beyond those repeaters to just two retransmissions. Set your TNC to beacon once every 30 minutes. That's sufficient for a fixed station.

If you are running APRS from a car, try...

WIDE1-1,WIDE2-1
(or APRS VIA WIDE1-1,WIDE2-1).

WIDE1-1 ensures that your packet will be picked up by at least one local (WIDE1) digipeater or a home station acting as a fill-in digipeater and relayed at least once. WIDE2-1 gets your packet to another, presumably wider-coverage digipeater, but limits the retransmissions beyond this point. It's wasteful of the network to set up wide coverage for a station that is rapidly changing its position anyway. (A guy 200 miles away isn't all that interested to

know which route you're taking to the grocery!) Mobile stations that are in motion should also limit their beacon rate to once every 60 seconds, or once per mile, whichever comes first.

Never invoke extremely wide coverage, such as a WIDE2-5 path, unless you are way out in the hinterlands and need every relaying station available to get your packets into the network.

It is worth noting that you can use aliases to limit the spread of your packets to specific areas. To keep my packets within the State of Connecticut, I can use the CTn-n alias in my path statement, like this: CT1-1, CT2-2

This path assures that local Connecticut stations (CT1-1) will repeat my packets, and that broad-coverage stations (CT2-2) will relay them throughout a large portion of the state. APRS digipeaters outside Connecticut, however, will not respond to these packets because they won't recognize the CT2-2 alias. My packets will still be heard across state boarders but will not be digipeated or add to the packet activity in a neighboring state.

Duplicate packet suppression

Now that APRS has finished flooding your data way too much, it also adds a means of suppressing too much flooding. Some APRS digipeaters keep a history of recently received packets (for the last 90 seconds, for example) and throw away any duplicates (based on the Information field remaining the same). Besides helping to solve a lot of looping, this technique also dampens the noise level coming from hams who set their APRS beacon intervals to unreasonable short times (e.g. one a second)!

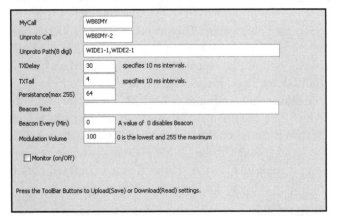

MyCall	WB8IMY	
Unproto Call	WB8IMY-2	
Unproto Path(8 digi)	WIDE1-1, WIDE2-1	
TXDelay	30	specifies 10 ms intervals.
TXTail	4	specifies 10 ms intervals.
Persistance(max 255)	64	
Beacon Text		
Beacon Every (Min)	0	A value of 0 disables Beacon
Modulation Volume	100	0 is the lowest and 255 the maximum

☐ Monitor (on/off)

Press the ToolBar Buttons to Upload(Save) or Download(Read) settings.

Setting up an APRS-compatible packet TNC for APRS. Notice the UNPROTO (path) statement.

APRS MESSAGES

We've now finished introducing the APRS digipeating infrastructure. What about the data that we've worked so hard to flood (and suppress)? APRS sends a variety of messages, including telemetry, short two-way text messages, bulletins, queries and replies.

APRS messages: Telemetry

APRS sends out a variety of status messages which include the time, latitude, longitude, altitude, heading and speed. Other data can include transmitter power, height, and gain, DF bearings, weather conditions and a variety of other objects. In fact, electronic home weather stations can be interfaced to GPS-compatible TNCs and their data

UI-View displays a weather bulletin in its message list.

transmitted over the APRS network. (Double click your mouse cursor on a weather station icon and you'll see a list of interesting weather stats such as wind speed, humidity levels and more.) Every TNC telemetry connection is different, so be sure to consult your TNC manual. In most cases, the same port is used to communicate with GPS receivers and weather stations—or any other data source such as a moisture sensor in your boat to let you know that it sprung a leak while you were away.

Since APRS is trying to cram a lot of information into a fairly low bandwidth channel, a number of compression techniques have been developed. These include reusing the destination call sign (you may have noticed that it's not really used for anything of importance) and compressing

position data to take up less space. An example of this is the APRS Mic-Encoder (Mic-E) compression shown in the following:

N2NWZ-4>T0TW4X,WIDE2-2:'eU0l'')v/]''4e

The destination call sign in the above humanly-unreadable example contains an encoded version of the position, as does the remaining message text. Mic-E encoding also supports the concept of SSID-encoding the digipeater path (which must be supported by the digipeater receiving the packet). By SSID-encoding, the packet can be shortened further, completely eliminating the digipeat path resulting in, for example:

N2NWZ-4>T0TW4X-3:'eU0l'')v/]''4e}

The use of SSID 3 above is equivalent to using WIDE3-3. Four bits of data already being sent results in 21 bytes of data not clogging the airwaves – saving 140 ms for each repetition of the packet.

Also of note is that SSIDs 8-15 allows the APRS digipeater administrator to determine the best next-hop digis in the indicated directions. For example, WB2ZII might use N2MH-15 (in West Orange, NJ) as the next hop for the West path.

APRS messages: Two-way text

So far, the APRS messages shown have been one-way announcements of a station's location, etc. APRS also supports two-way reliable messaging. One can send a short text message to a specific station and that station, upon receipt of the message, will send back an acknowledgement:

N2YGK>APX104,WIDE2-2::N2NWZ-2 :I'm tracking the trail now!{4

N2NWZ-2>APW246,WIDE2-2::N2YGK :ack4

If no ACK is received, the sending station periodically retransmits the message. One problem for APRS messaging is the appropriate selection of the correct digipeater path to get the message there. "Smart" implementations of APRS use the last received packet from the recipient to derive a reasonably good path.

APRS messages: Bulletins

APRS Bulletins are one-way short messages. Rather than being addressed to a specific station, they are sent to the special call sign BLNn. BLN1 is shown on line 1 of the bulletins display, BLN2 on line 2 and so on. Bulletins should be used sparingly or not at all:

KC2GMM>APR851,WIDE2-2::BLN1 :Welcome HAMS NYC marathon.{11}

KC2GMM>APR851,WIDE2-2::BLN2 :Anyone know freqs for race?{16}

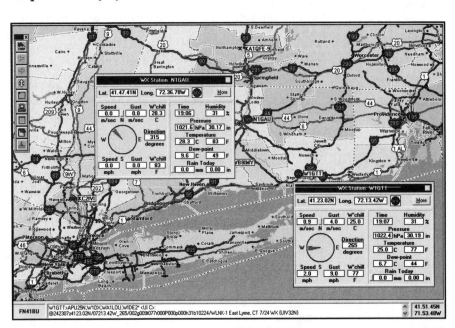

When you double click on weather station icons in *UI-View*, windows open to display the latest reported weather data such as temperature, wind direction, wind speed and more. Other APRS applications function in a similar manner.

APRS messages: Queries/Replies

APRS supports a variety of general and directed (addressed to a single recipient) queries and their replies. Some of these include:

- ?APRS Query for what other APRS stations are on frequency. Is typically used when a new stations comes up and wants to get an up to date status. The query can be constrained to a circle around a given latitude and longitude in which case only stations within that circle reply.

- ?APRSD Asks for a list of stations heard direct. Useful for mapping out propagation given that the reporting stations typically have announced their location, altitude, and approximate EIRP.

- ?APRSH Asks if you've heard a particular station.

- ?WX Solicits weather telemetry from APRS stations equipped with automated weather measurement equipment. A number of home weather stations such as those manufactured by Davis and Peet Brothers will interface directly with packet TNCs for APRS applications. Their beacon information contains informative data on wind speed, wind direction, temperature, humidity and much more.

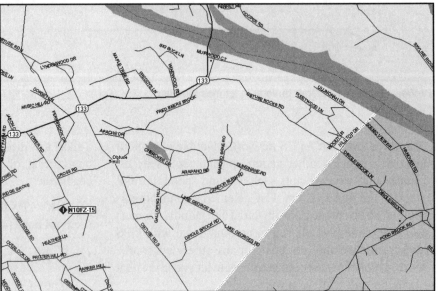

The N1OFZ IGate station appears on an APRS map. IGates act as gateways to and from the Internet.

IGATES AND THE INTERNET

The APRS network is not a continuous VHF or UHF system stretching from coast to coast and border to border. There are gaps in coverage where one subset of the network is isolated from the rest. Fortunately, APRS uses the Internet to act as a bridge between these areas, unifying the network nationwide.

It does this fascinating trick through the use of specialized stations known as Internet Gateways, or simply *IGates*. IGate stations run dedicated software that takes all received packets and transfers them to APRS Internet servers. Depending on how the IGate owner has configured his station, this can be a two-way process

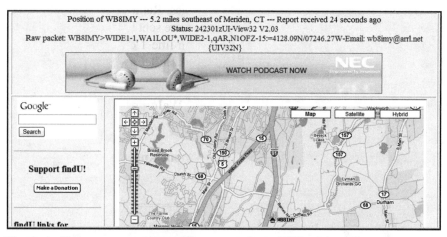

Thanks to IGates, you can see position reports from APRS stations throughout the country by simply opening a Web browser and doing a query of the FINDU and APRSWorld databases. Several Web sites provide the ability to do this, such as "Wulfden" at www.wulfden.org/APRSQuery.shtml.

with packets also entering local networks from distant locations through the IGate. If you see an icon from a station on the opposite side of the continent, chances are the data reached you through a nearby IGate (or the mother of all VHF bands openings is taking place!). To keep congestion to a minimum, however, most IGates limit the amount of "DX" they relay to the local network.

Thanks to IGates and the APRS Internet servers, it is possible to see position reports from APRS stations throughout the country by simply opening a Web browser and doing a query of the FINDU and APRSWorld databases. Several Web sites provide the ability to do this, such as "Wulfden" at **www.wulfden.org/APRSQuery.shtml**.

By entering a call sign in the query box, you can see the last reported position of any APRS station whose packets have managed to reach an IGate portal. Try it yourself. Go to the Wulfden site and enter W1AW, the call sign of the ARRL Headquarters station. You'll see the W1AW position displayed on a map along with the actual "raw" data of the last packet received.

This ability can come in handy when you are traveling and you want your friends and family to be able to monitor your progress. *Anyone* can use these lookup sites (ham license not required), so all you have to do is give them the Web URL and tell them to enter your call sign in the query field.

PACKET AND PUBLIC SERVICE

One of the more innovative uses of packet radio technology in recent years has been in public service operations. "Public Service" can mean emergency support, but it can also mean support in non-emergency situations, such as providing communications for a parade or other activity.

AUTOMATIC POSITION REPORTING SYSTEM (APRS)

With its ability to track moving objects, APRS is a "natural" for public service work. An APRS station at a central location, such as an Emergency Operations Center (EOC), can display the movements of amateurs throughout a wide area. If the EOC is blessed with an LCD projector, you could even project the APRS screen on a large wall display for all to see.

For this type of application to work properly, each tracked amateur must have a 2-meter FM transceiver, a GPS receiver and a packet radio TNC or tracker as described in Chapter 2. There are some potential pitfalls that you may need to address:

■ The tracked amateurs may be forced to use low power and compromise antennas. A typical example is a ham with a 5-W handheld transceiver and a "rubber duck" antenna. Such a station may have only a marginal signal back to the EOC, insufficient to decode and display.

■ Tracked amateurs with higher output and better antennas will require "mobile" stations that lack easy portability. They may consist of hams driving their own vehicles, or higher-powered mobile installations in agency vehicles.

■ Rugged terrain can create difficult signal paths, as can a forest of tall buildings in urban settings. This can result in poor coverage and unreliable tracking. One solution is to build and deploy portable digipeaters powered

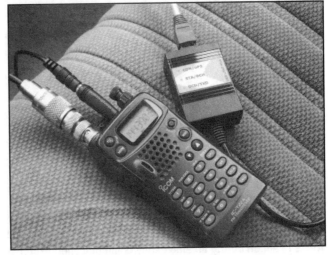

A handheld radio can be turned into an APRS tracker by adding a GPS receiver and a tracking TNC.

by batteries or other sources. See **Figure 3-1**. These portable digis can be scattered at advantageous points throughout the area to help fill coverage gaps (**Figure 3-2**). Everyone in the network would have to configure their TNC UNPROTO path statements to include the digipeater call signs or aliases.

It is also possible to attach low-power APRS tracking

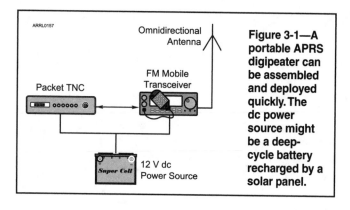

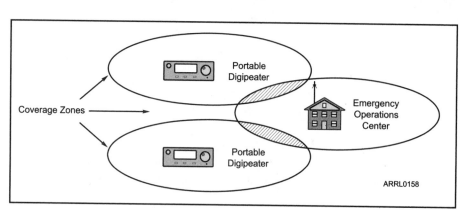

Figure 3-1—A portable APRS digipeater can be assembled and deployed quickly. The dc power source might be a deep-cycle battery recharged by a solar panel.

Figure 3-2—Strategically placed digipeaters can extend APRS coverage.

units to vehicles and other moving objects without the need for an amateur onboard. A string of parade floats could be tracked in this fashion, for example. The same power and antenna considerations apply, though. Cost is a factor as well. A typical APRS tracking package could cost $300 or more, and clubs could find it difficult to afford a collection of such devices.

The technical issues notwithstanding, many amateurs have made good use of APRS in public service applications. Storm spotters have used APRS to quickly relay their locations back to operators at weather centers. Automated APRS weather stations (see Chapter 2) have been valuable resources in determining the strength and movement of severe weather systems. In the western US, hams have attached small APRS trackers to search and rescue dogs to track their movements! APRS trackers have also been used to monitor the positions of boats in a community river race. And last but not least, some public-service networks use APRS exchanging short text messages during emergency operations.

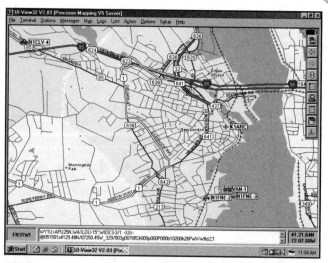

APRS in action during an emergency communication exercise in New London, CT.

This BeeLine GPS tracker combines the GPS receiver, TNC and FM transmitter into a tiny package weighing only two ounces. On the Web at **http://bigredbee.com/**.

WINLINK 2000

If you've heard of Winlink 2000 at all, you probably think of it as an HF application. In truth, there is considerable Winlink 2000 activity on VHF as a network of packet stations linked through Internet gateways. The major attraction of Winlink 2000 is that it gives hams and served agencies the ability to reach the Internet via RF pathways to exchange vital e-mails, some of which may include file attachments such as supply lists and even small images.

Winlink 2000 Evolution

The Winlink network evolved in the mid 1990s from the original AMTOR based APLink system, authored by Victor D. Poor, W5SMM. APLink was a network of stations that relayed messages to and from each other and the VHF packet network. As PCs became more powerful, and as the PACTOR protocols superseded AMTOR, a new software system was needed. That need brought about the debut of Winlink Classic, authored by Poor, with additions from Peter Schultz, TY1PS.

Winlink itself evolved with substantial enhancements courtesy of Hans Kessler, N8PGR. To bring the Internet into the picture Winlink stations needed an e-mail agent to interface with cyberspace. To meet that requirement Steve Waterman, K4CJX, enlisted the help of Jim Jennings, W5EUT and Rick Muething, KN6KB, to add Netlink to Winlink Classic.

Early in 2000, the system took a major technological and evolutionary leap, becoming a full-featured Internet-to-RF "star network" gateway system known as Winlink 2000 or "WL2K." Today Winlink 2000 is an international network of participating stations. The network is comprised of PACTOR mailbox operations (PMBOs) on the HF bands and TelPac packet stations on VHF and UHF, all connected via the Internet to a central server (CMBO) hub.

When disaster strikes, it usually causes power and Internet disruption over a confined area. This area might be the size of a small town, or it could cover an entire state. Outside the disaster area, however, power and Internet access are still available. By using VHF packet links Winlink 2000 can provide "last mile" connectivity beyond the

disaster site to a point where the Internet is still available. See **Figure 3-3**. It is also possible to create HF links to span greater distances.

With an RF link to the Internet, hams and other volunteers can quickly communicate with the outside world. Once an e-mail message reaches the Winlink 2000 system via the Internet, it becomes available to any authorized individual with Internet access. For example, Amateur Radio volunteers might use the Winlink 2000 system to send an e-mail request for medical supplies to a Red Cross facility outside the disaster area. Workers at the distant Red Cross center can also send e-mail replies to the amateurs in the field. As far as the Red Cross workers are concerned, the exchange looks as though it is taking place entirely via the Internet.

Winlink Access

To access Winlink 2000 on VHF, you must have a computer, a packet radio TNC and an FM voice transceiver—the same basic packet station described in Chapter 1. Most Winlink 2000 VHF operations use 1200 baud packet and this works well if the e-mails are strictly text messages. To handle e-mails with file attachments, it is best to use 9600 baud.

Your ultimate goal is to establish a connection to a Winlink 2000 *TelPac* station. A TelPac station has reliable access to the Internet, usually through a broadband connection. It will function as your gateway to the outside world. You can link to the TelPac station directly, or through nodes or digipeaters. There are many TelPac stations in continuous operation throughout the country. You'll find a list at **www.winlink.org/status/TelPacStatus.aspx**.

To send and receive e-mail through Winlink 2000, you'll also need a piece of *Windows* software known as *AirMail*. It is downloadable free on the Web at **www.siriuscyber.net/ham/**. *AirMail* functions much like a traditional e-mail application. In fact, it is designed to look very much like Microsoft *Outlook*, and to be just as easy to use. Every ham in the field who intends to access the Winlink 2000 network must have *AirMail* installed on his computer. There is an *AirMail* alternative known as *Paclink*, which we'll discuss later.

Installing and Configuring AirMail

When you open *AirMail*, you will see a screen similar to the one shown in **Figure 3-4**. Click your mouse cursor on Tools, then Options then the Modules tab. Click the VHF Packet Setup box

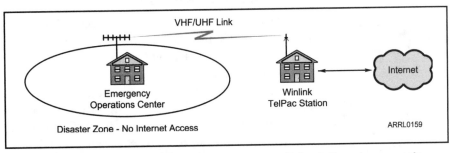

Figure 3-3—Winlink 2000 on VHF functions as a "last mile" solution when agencies need Internet e-mail access. In this example, a VHF link out of the disaster zone allows e-mail to be sent via the nearest TelPac station.

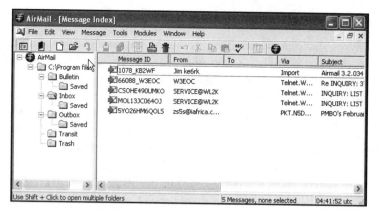

Figure 3-4—The *AirMail* main screen.

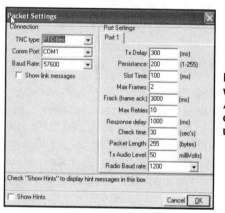

Figure 3-5—In this window you "tell" *AirMail* what type of TNC you are using.

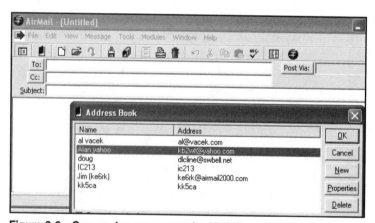

Figure 3-6—Composing a message in *AirMail*.

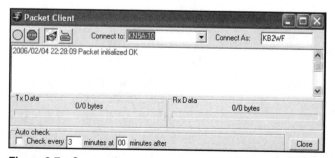

Figure 3-7—Connecting and sending your *AirMail* message.

and click the **SETUP** button to choose your packet TNC and configure the other settings. Also click **Auto Start** and **Show in Tool Bar**. Auto Start will start the packet client as soon as you start AirMail. Make sure your TNC is connected and on or Auto Start will fail. Put a checkmark in the box to the left of "VHF Packet Client" then click the **SETUP** button.

Clicking on **SETUP** should open a window similar to the one in **Figure 3-5**. In this window you need to "tell" *AirMail* what type of TNC you are using, the computer COM port you have the TNC attached to and the baud rate the TNC is using to communicate with the computer. At the time of this writing, *AirMail* supported only the following TNCs:

AEA/Timewave PK232 and PK900

Kantronics KPC3 and KPC3+, KPC9612 and KPC9612+, KAM and KAM+, KAM98 and KAMXL

SCS PTC-II, PTC-IIe, PTC-IIex, PTC-IIpro

You can use the default port settings, although you will need to change the "Radio Baud Rate" if you are using 9600 baud packet. Click the **OK** button and you're done.

Composing a Message in AirMail

In the main *AirMail* screen, click the third icon from the left (you should see "Format a New Message" as your mouse cursor hovers over the icon). This will bring up the window where you will enter the destination e-mail address and compose your message. See **Figure 3-6**. If the destination address is on the Internet, you simply enter it as you would any other Internet address in ordinary e-mail. Composing your message works the same way. You can attach files at this point, but make sure they are relatively small. If you are operating at 1200 baud, limit the attachment size to about 15 Kbytes.

Note the POST VIA field in this window. If you are connecting to a Winlink 2000 TelPac station, it should read **WL2K**. When you are ready, click on the little mailbox button and your e-mail will be moved to the "Outbox" for transmission.

Connecting to a TelPac Station

Let's assume that you want to connect to TelPac station KN5A-10. On the mail *AirMail* screen (Figure 3-4), click on Modules, then Packet Client. You should see the window shown in **Figure 3-7**.

In the **Connect to** box, insert the call sign of the TelPac station you are contacting (KN5A-10 in this example). In the **Connect As** box, check that your call sign is correct. If you need to connect through a digipeater, this is where you enter the digipeater call sign after your own, separated by a single space. *Do not* add a V,

VIA or any other characters.

Click on the *automatic handshake* icon. This is the easiest way to connect. This enables *AirMail* to handle all the connections and instructions to start, send posted messages, pick up waiting messages and disconnect when finished. This is much quicker than the keyboard mode, which is only used for special purposes.

As your station connects and begins exchanging e-mail, you should see the red transmit light on your TNC blink. Then you should see your receive light blink if a reply is received. Both lights will alternate on and off. If the other station cannot be contacted, the TNC will time out after a fixed number of tries

As the transfer progresses, you will see codes being sent and also the file transfer rate, either transmit or receive, if an attachment is being sent. Finally, you will see an "FQ" and then a disconnect message. Your list of posted messages should now have a check mark to indicate that they have been successfully sent.

Your message is now in the hands of the TelPac station, which will automatically forward it to the Internet. Within seconds your e-mail will be sitting in the recipient's Internet e-mail box. Your address will appear to them as **<Your Call Sign>@winlink.org**. If they respond to your e-mail, it will automatically route back to the Winlink 2000 central server and will be available the next time you access a TelPac station—*any* TelPac station.

The Paclink Alternative

Paclink is a Winlink application that does much of what we've already described, but it uses Microsoft *Outlook* as the e-mail client. *Paclink* supports more TNC models than *AirMail*, including a sound card TNC, and it also allows you to use tactical call signs such as "EOC1" rather than W6XYZ. There are significant issues to consider, however:

■ You must download the *AGW Packet Engine* (AGWPE) software (**www.elcom.gr/sv2agw/inst.htm**).

■ You must download *Paclink AGW* and *Paclink Post Office* from **www.winlink.org/Client.htm** (scroll to the bottom of the page).

■ Your computer must be running *Windows XP* or *2000*.

■ Your computer must have Microsoft *.Net Framework* installed. This is freely downloadable from Microsoft.

Setting up a *Paclink* station is substantially more complicated than configuring a station for use with *AirMail*. That's why a number of amateurs choose *AirMail* for VHF Winlink access. As this book was being written, the Winlink development group was working on a new version of *Paclink* that will be much easier to install.

But until that day arrives, you need to download the software noted above and follow these simplified steps to create your Paclink station.

(1) If your computer doesn't have Microsoft *.Net Framework* installed, get on the Web and go to **www.microsoft.com**. In the **SEARCH** box, enter NET Framework and you will find the download page. Download the file and install.

(2) Run *AGWPE*. Once it is running, it will place two icons in your lower right-hand desktop tray. Right click the icon that resembles two radio towers. Click **PROPERTIES**, then **New Port**. Configure a port according to the TNC you are using. Exit *AGWPE*.

(3) Run *Paclink Post Office* and configure it by entering your call sign and password. Accept defaults for everything else. You have to connect to a Winlink TelPac station and use it before you're actually registered in the Winlink system and receive a password, but go ahead and put password in the field anyway. During the initial setup, *Paclink Post Office* will automatically create an *Outlook* e-mail account using your call sign. Check your *Outlook* accounts after the setup and you will see it listed. It will be set as the default account, but you can easily change this. Check the account to make sure your Winlink password is there.

(4) Now run *Paclink AGW*, click **FILE** and make sure you have entered correct path to the *AGWPE* software on your hard drive. Next you'll need to set up a "channel" in *Paclink AGW*. Click **FILE** then **CHANNEL**. Set up the channel accordingly. Note the field for the call sign of the "remote station." This is the call sign of the TelPac station you will be connecting to on this channel. If you have several TelPac stations that you may be using, you can create separate channels for each.

(5) With everything finally configured, you can start the system by running *AGWPE*, then *Paclink AGW* (*Paclink AGW* will start *Paclink Postoffice* automatically). Alternatively, you can have *AGWPE* start *Paclink AGW* when it starts. (Right click *AGWPE* icon, then click **STARTUP PROGRAMS**.)

Open *Outlook* and compose a message. When you are finished, click **SEND** just as you would for normal Internet e-mail. If the Winlink account is the default, it should start trying to connect to the designated TelPac station through the *Paclink AGW*. When connected, it will send the message and download waiting e-mail.

For a more detailed description of this process, download the excellent tutorial in PDF format at **www.winlink.org/Presentations/Paclink%20AGW%20Install.pdf**.

Establishing a Winlink 2000 TelPac Station

Winlink 2000 TelPac stands for TELnet PACket gateway. It functions as the gateway between packet users in the field and the Internet Winlink 2000 network.

To set up a TelPac station you must have the following:

■ A connection to the Internet, preferably DSL or broadband cable
■ A computer running *Windows XP* or *Vista*
■ An FM transceiver and antenna
■ A packet radio TNC

TelPac stations can be permanent or portable as the need requires. Since the TelPac station is the key link in the chain back to the Internet, it is best to use good antennas and higher output power to ensure reliable coverage.

TelPac installation itself is straightforward. See **Figure 3-8**.

First download the *TelPac.exe* self-extracting zip file which contains the install program and documentation (about 2.5 Meg). Go to **www.winlink.org/Client.htm**, scroll down to the section on TelPac and download the file. Run the file and put the zipped files into a temporary folder. You should see the *Setup.exe*, *SETUP.LST* and *TelPac.CAB* files. Double click on the *Setup.exe* to begin installation.

Registration

You don't have to register your TelPac gateway, but it is a good idea. With your TelPac registered in the system, users will be about to look it up online easily and determine when it is operational. TelPacs now can automatically "check in" periodically to WL2K, which keeps statistics on gateway activity. You can see real-time TelPac status on a map display at **www.Winlink.org/positions/telpacpos.aspx**.

When you run the TelPac software for the first time, it will ask you to register the product. You *can* run the program without registration, but you will get the "nag" pop up each time it is started. Registration is free and easy. Just go to **www.winlink.org/status/TelPacEx.aspx**, enter your station gateway call sign including any –SSID desired. Most TelPac gateways select an SSID of –10. When you have completed the entry you will see the registration number in bold letters at the top of the page. This number can be entered at the nag prompt when you start TelPac again.

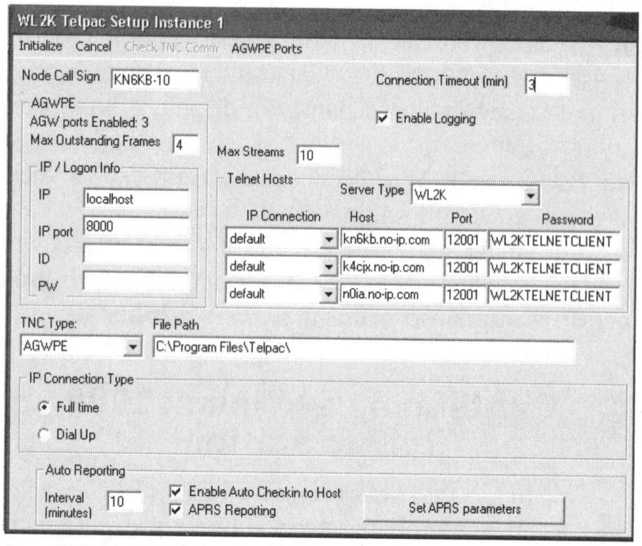

AGW Packet Engine (AGWPE) Setup

Your first decision on setup is whether you will use the *AGW Packet Engine* to interface the TNC(s) to TelPac, or just use the TNC directly. The advantage of *AGWPE* is that it supports more TNC types and it allows reliable use of multiple streams. The later can be important in an emergency application where you may have several field stations connecting at the same time.

AGWPE is available in two formats. *Packet Engine Pro* has a 30 day evaluation period and costs $49 after that. The *AGW Packet Engine* is free for amateur use, but is more difficult to set up. Both can be downloaded at **www.elcom.gr/sv2agw**.

Let's take a look at the steps necessary to run a TelPac setup with *AGWPE* first. Before doing anything else, you must install and test *AGWPE* (or Pro) and make sure it is working properly. Don't proceed with the TelPac setup until you know you have a working *AGW* installation.

When you register your TelPac station, or decline registration, the next menu you will see is the TelPac setup. This is where you must decide whether you are going to use *AGWPE* or just a TNC by itself. Look for the "TNC Types" selection box. For now, let's assume that you have *AGWPE* installed. We'll cover TNC-only installations later.

Enter the gateway call sign you wish to use for this TelPac "instance," as it is called. This should be the same call sign you registered. The field Max Outstanding Frames is used to meter the outbound flow to avoid channel hogging. Normally values of 1-3 are fine for busy-to-average channels. Higher numbers (6-10) can increase channel throughput at the expense of increased channel "hogging".

If *AGWPE* is running on the same computer as TelPac you can leave the ID and PW fields blank. An IP address of "localhost" will normally resolve to your local computer but try 127.0.0.1 if localhost does not work. *AGWPE* is usually set up with a default port of 8000 but if yours was not enter the IP Port number in the IP port field.

The Connection Timeout is a mechanism that will automatically disconnect a connected station if there has been no response after the preset time. Usually 5 minutes is good for *AGWPE* installations.

The Max Streams parameter determines how many simultaneous connections (from all ports) will be supported. This can be set from 0-10. A value of 0 will disable *all* inbound connections.

Checking the Enable Logging checkbox will enable

Figure 3-8—The TelPac configuration screen.

the TelPac log that will log all connects by call letter and time, so you'll be able to see who has been accessing your station. Logging will not include the Stream Monitor window of the main menu unless the Save Monitor to Log button is manually clicked.

Your TelPac station must be able to reach a Winlink Telnet server on the Internet and it does this through a Telnet connection. The TelPac software has a built-in server list and in most cases this will be adequate. You can select a first and second backup Telnet host. If a connection cannot be made to the primary, the backup Telnet servers will be tried automatically.

It is recommended you also check Enable Auto Check-in and set a period (nominally 15-30 minutes for full time connections). When this option is checked TelPac will periodically log in briefly as the gateway call sign. This allows WL2K to capture stats and be able to show which TelPac gateways are active on the status Web page. Recommended check-in intervals are 15-30 minutes for a full time connection and 60-180 minutes for a dial-up connection. Each auto check-in session is logged and the last check-in is shown on the main TelPac menu. If the sysop menu is being used and the sysop is logged in auto check-in will be disabled.

Once all the appropriate fields are set up, click **Initialize** on the setup menu (upper left corner). This will save the settings and attempt the connection to the *AGWPE*. *AGWPE* will, in turn, communicate with your TNC, placing it in the KISS mode.

As TelPac attempts to initialize, you may see an error message to the effect that banner_1.txt can't be found. If so, use *Windows Notepad* to open Examplebanner_1.txt in the TelPac directory and edit it to include your TelPac call sign and any other message you wish connecting stations to see. Save this file as Banner_1.txt.

TNC (No AGW) Setup

You'll need to begin by creating custom initialization file for your TNC. In the TelPac directory on your hard drive you will find several TNC files with names like ExampleKPC3_1.aps, ExampleKAM_1.aps etc. These are example files and can be used as templates. You will have to edit the one of these that applies to the TNC you will use and save it as KPC3_1.aps or KAM_1.aps etc (without the preface "Example"). Use a simple text editor (like *Windows Notepad*) and save the files as text files with the *exact* names shown. The call sign you will enter in the TelPac software Setup menu will override any MYCall settings in the TNC or in the .aps file.

Now start the TelPac program and follow the registration and setup instructions as for the *AGWPE* setup except for the Serial port setup data. If you select a TNC type other than "*AGWPE*" on the setup page you will see a menu similar to the one shown in **Figure 3-9**. In Figure

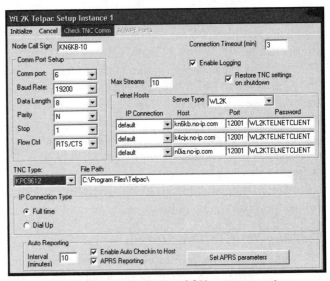

Figure 3-9—Setting up the TelPac COM port parameters.

3-9 the *AGWPE* setup frame is replaced by the COM Port setup frame. Set the serial port parameters here. Parameters on the left are used to select the COM port parameters, flow control mechanism and TNC Type. You should use hardware flow control RTS/CTS. Once all parameters are selected you can test the communications to the TNC using the Check TNC COM menu item. If the baud rate and COM port parameters are OK you should get a positive check. The check will work if the TNC is in any interface mode.

The other setup fields are similar to what was described in the *AGWPE* setup. The differences are:
- You have a check box option to restore the TNC to its initial settings. Check this if you need to leave the TNC unaltered on exit.
- The *AGWPE* Ports menu is disabled and the Check TNC COM menu is enabled. This allows easy verification of serial port settings and communications with the TNC.
- You should use a larger Connection Timeout value when sending large files. This is because the TNC does not provide explicit information on what packets have actually been sent. A value of 10-20 minutes should cover most practical file sizes.

In the IP Connection Type frame you must select whether you are using a full time (cable, DSL or LAN type) connection or a dial up connection for connecting to the WL2K Telnet Server via the Internet. The full time connection is recommended for minimal latency, but a dial-on-demand mechanism is also available for dial up only connections.

You can initialize the TNC by clicking the **Initialize** menu item. This will take several seconds depending on the TNC and baud rate. An initialization form will show the progress and should close automatically if successful.

If initialization fails try other communication parameters and make sure the TNC and computer are connected by a proper cable (Including RTS and CTS signals) and the TNC is set for the matching comm. parameters.

As with the *AGWPE* setup previously, you may see an error message to the effect that banner_1.txt can't be found. If so, use *Windows Notepad* to open Examplebanner_1.txt and edit it to include your TelPac call sign and any other message you wish connecting stations to see. Save this file as Banner_1.txt.

After a successful initialization the next time you start TelPac the TNC should initialize automatically.

Starting Your TelPac Station

You can start the TelPac program by using the *Windows* Start, Programs, TelPac or by double clicking the TelPac icon in the installation directory. You can of course put short cuts to start the program on your desktop or startup directories. If you are using *AGW Packet Engine* the recommend way is to have the *Packet Engine* start *TelPac* automatically after the *Packet Engine* has initialized.

See the operating menu in **Figure 3-10**. It shows the TNC Status and COM port and all active connections to the TelPac gateway. The right side shows all the connections (Up to 10 depending on your settings for Max Streams). When a connection is active it's Stream (A-J), Port number (1-20) and call sign of the connecting station is shown and the background becomes yellow. The traffic indicator shows the direction by arrow and color of the last packet sent to or received by the connected station. For each stream there is a "radio style" selector button for monitoring. When selected, new traffic for that stream will be shown in the monitor window. If the monitor radio style button is selected on an active link the manual disconnect button will be enabled. This allows a sysop to force a disconnect after answering YES to the confirmation request.

The left most character in the monitor window shows

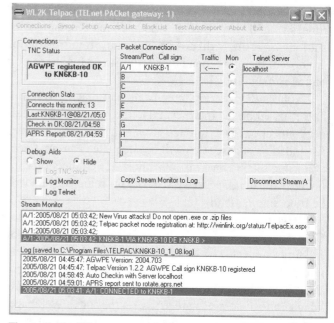

Figure 3-10—When you see this screen, your Winlink 2000 TelPac station is up and running.

the stream (A-J)) and will be capitalized for data originating from the TelPac gateway and lower case for data originating from the remote connected station. The second number is the port number (1-20). The right hand column identifies the active Telnet server being used for each connection. Normally this would be the primary server unless the primary were not available or has reached its maximum number of connections.

With the TelPac software up and running, your TelPac station is on the air and ready to receive e-mail from the Internet or via packet radio. Check the activity in your area before choosing the frequency for your TelPac station. Most TelPac stations in the United States are operating on 2 meters between 145.00 and 145.70 MHz.

AD HOC PACKET NETWORKS WITH *OUTPOST*

Ad Hoc is Latin for "to this" or "to this purpose." In this chapter we use it to refer to packet networks that are dedicated to one purpose—public service. The network may be available continuously, or it may be set up "on the fly" to provide communications at an event or disaster site.

Amateur Radio Emergency Service (ARES) groups have been putting 1200 and 9600-baud packet radio to work in this application for a number of years. Since there are so many TNCs available, and since almost any modern FM transceiver can instantly become a data radio, packet networks are relatively easy to establish as the need arises.

Public service packet can be made even more efficient through the use of software designed for the application. One such program that has gained a great deal of attention in recent years is *Outpost* for *Windows*, created by Jim Oberhofer, KN6PE. *Outpost* is available at no charge and can be downloaded on the Web at **www.outpostpm. org/**.

Outpost is a PC-based messaging application that simplifies the process of passing emergency packet traffic. By hiding the complexity of the TNC and BBS command-set and simplifying the mechanics for managing messages, the thinking was that *Outpost* could be used in a similar manner as other contemporary e-mail clients (like Microsoft's *Windows Mail* and *Outlook*). There are plenty of people who use e-mail that do not know how a message gets from here to there. *Outpost* attempts to do something similar with packet messaging.

Outpost is not a complete packet environment. Instead, it is a messaging client that plugs into the existing AX.25 packet infrastructure. *Outpost* uses any existing BBS or PBBS (there are probably a couple in your area today) as mail drops where *Outpost* can send messages for pickup by other users or to be forwarded to another BBS. With only your existing TNC, a radio, and a *Windows*-based PC, you tell *Outpost* about who you are (your call sign), the TNC, and the BBS. *Outpost* then manages all message-handling between your PC and the BBS.

How Outpost works

If you are a current AX.25 packet user, you will recognize the steps: boot up your PC, run your favorite terminal emulator, power up your TNC and radio, and check the TNC (or interface) settings. Connect to your local BBS, check for and retrieve any personal messages, bulletins of interest, or NTS messages, send any outgoing messages, and then exit from the BBS. If you are operating during an emergency, you may be waiting for information and have to repeat these steps several times.

Outpost takes care of most of the above steps. Whatever a user would normally type at the keyboard, *Outpost* does automatically in an automated terminal emulation mode. Because you have previously told *Outpost* all about the TNC and BBS prompts and commands, *Outpost* essentially reads and interprets the messages sent back by the TNC or BBS to determine when they are ready to accept another command (just like you would do), then sends and processes all TNC and BBS commands and replies during a "Send/Receive Session."

Once you initiate a Send/Receive session (just a push of a button), *Outpost* sets up the TNC or selected interface, connects to the BBS, sends all messages from its out-tray destined for this BBS, requests the list of messages based on the message types you selected, reads each message, stores it in the in-tray, deletes the retrieved message off of the BBS (if allowed), then exits. *Outpost* can be configured to periodically repeat this process automatically, essentially operating in an unattended mode.

Features

All of *Outpost*'s features align with its mission to support emergency packet communications. While there are plenty of things it can do, the top 10 features are:

- Supports all three packet message types: Private, NTS and Bulletins.
- Messages can be created from scratch, imported from an ASCII file, cut and pasted in from other applica-

tions, or by Replying to or Forwarding a previously received message.
- Create messages with the built-in NTS Message Maker, a forms-based menu that prompts the user for all required fields, then creates a correctly formatted and addressed NTS packet message. ARL Messages can also be selected and automatically formatted.
- Use the online report interpreter that helps get a predefined report templates filled out, formatted, and sent quickly.
- Supports serial TNCs, *AGWPE*, and Telnet interfacing.
- *Outpost* can use several popular PBBS and BBSs as mail drops including Winlink via TelPac.
- You can reach these BBSs by configuring for either direct access, going through one or more digipeater stations, or through a series of nodes.
- When multiple *Outpost* stations are in use, the originator can flag a message as Urgent (shows up in RED at the recipient's station), or request delivery and read receipts.
- *Outpost* can automatically initiate packet sessions with a BBS either at some predefined interval, or by defining up to 4 absolute times over the course of an hour (i.e.: 5 minutes after the hour, 20 after, 35 after, 50 after).
- Tactical Calls can makes a field assignment "operator neutral," thereby allowing the operators to change without having the assignment name change. *Outpost* implements Tactical Calls by taking advantage of specific BBS behaviors while still operating within the FCC rules.

Getting The Most Out Of Your Packet Operations

We've seen what *Outpost* can do and how it has been deployed. In the examples described above, and during most packet emergency deployments, somebody, sooner or later, makes some decisions on how to use it so that the messages keep flowing. Ideally, these decisions were considered up front, and essentially manifest themselves in an organization's *Packet Policy*. A policy is defined as a course of action, guiding principle, or procedure that is considered expedient, prudent or advantageous.

During an emergency, we operate within a certain protocol to manage nets and exchange messages. This also applies to packet. With the above definition in mind and in a community of packet users, packet policies should be defined to help support order, consistency, and efficiency with how packet is deployed and used. Packet Policies also need to be designed specifically with the needs of the emergency response team and served agencies in mind. While there is no single answer or official set of packet policies, the following is a good starting list of packet policy statements that an emergency communications team might consider adopting or adapting for their local packet operations. Other policy statements may be developed as necessary.

- All stations will identify with a tactical call sign
- All messages exchanged between 2 stations are sent as private messages
- All messages are uniquely identified
- All messages are as short as possible
- All stations will poll the BBS for messages no less than every 15 minutes
- All stations will poll for Private and Bulletin message types
- All packet message traffic becomes part of the official event documentation package

Outpost's evolution has been based on the input from packet users, many of whom needed a capability added to *Outpost* that implied a policy need. Several changes were implemented to satisfy these needs, and in almost all cases, these needs addressed an implicitly stated policy that was aimed to improve overall packet operations. Here's how *Outpost* implements these policies:

Policy #1: Identify with a Tactical Call Sign

Amateur Radio voice nets have used tactical call signs for years. However, the flexibility of Tactical Calls has been elusive in the packet radio world due to a variety of limitations and constraints. Ideally, Tactical Call support should be implemented at the BBS. However, it appears that all out-of-the-box BBSs do not explicitly support the use of Tactical Calls. *Outpost* implements Tactical Calls on the *Outpost* (client) side.

Given the current BBS designs, the approach for using Tactical Calls is essentially to find and adopt a call sign structure that satisfies the BBS' call sign checking logic while still making sense in your organization. For instance, through limited experimentation with the F6FBB BBS and KPC-3 PBBS, one valid BBS call sign format that could be used as a tactical call is as follows:

#xxxxx, where:
#is a number.
xxxxx   is any combinations of 5 letters.

The best way to understand Tactical Calls is to look at an example. In Santa Clara County, the County Hospital system implemented a packet network for its 11 regional hospitals using the F6FBB BBS as its packet mail drop. These hospitals were assigned a tactical call with the structure described above. For instance:

   1MVECH - Mountain View El Camino Hospital
   1PASMC - Palo Alto Stanford Medical Center
   1SJVMC - San Jose Valley Medical Center
   1SJGSH - San Jose Good Samaritan Hospital

For the Hospital system, the basic tactical call format that is used is:

1 CC HHH

-- the number "1"; arbitrary, satisfies the BBS need to see a digit

--2 letters for the city in which the hospital is located

--3 letter abbreviation for the hospital name

What does your BBS support? The first step is to determine a tactical call structure. Whereas F6FBB and KPC3 PBBSs support the example above, not all BBSs behave the same. From the *Outpost*, select **Tools > Interactive Packet** or some other packet program, and set the TNC "mycall" to your test "tactical call".

Connect to the BBS. At this point, you are connecting with your tactical call and not your legal call sign. Verify that the BBS accepts the call sign. If the connect is successful, register the Tactical Call with the BBS if you are prompted. Try sending yourself a message (round trip). If successful, you have a valid tactical call format.

Now we're ready to configure *Outpost*. From the main menu, select **Setup > Identification**. Check the "Use Tactical Call..." box, enter your Tactical Call in the "Tactical Call" field, and fill in the "ID Text String" (will be part of the transmitted legal identification string at the end of an *Outpost* Session).

At this point, when you start a new message, it will open with 1SJVMC set as the FROM address. When connecting to the BBS, *Outpost* will look for messages addressed to 1SJVMC

To turn off Tactical Calls, go to **Setup > Identification**, and uncheck the "Use Tactical Call..." box. All subsequent message and BBS processing will occur with your legal call sign. See **Figure 3-11**.

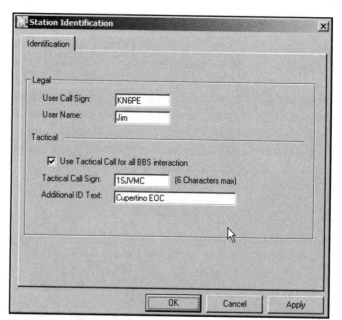

Figure 3-11—To turn off Tactical Calls, go to Setup > Identification, and uncheck the "Use Tactical Call..." box.

Policy #2: Messages Sent Between Stations Are Sent As Private

While this policy may seem obvious, it is not uncommon to find new packet users sending messages as bulletins. Inappropriate bulletin message traffic is one of the big contributors to channel congestion since every station checking for a valid bulletin gets to read your private message to your intended recipient.

Outpost helps control this by defaulting bulletins to Private (Tools > Message Settings, New Messages Tab). In general, do not send bulletins unless they really are (i) intended for a broad audience and (ii) the message is critical in nature.

Policy #3: All Messages Are Uniquely Identified

In voice nets, we number or serialize our message so that we can keep track of what was sent and received as well as allowing us to reply to a specific message more efficiently. The same applies should apply to packet messaging. The trick is finding a significantly unique identifier scheme that allows many stations operate within a packet network to pass uniquely identified messages without the risk of duplicating a message identifier. One way of deriving a message identifier is to create a message numbering scheme that embeds information about the originator with a number.

Outpost supports this by creating a concatenated unique message identifier based on the 3 character *Tactical ID* and the *Next Message Number*, both defined from the **Tools > Reports Settings** Menu, then turning it on from the **Tools > Message Settings** Menu, New Message Tab, and clicking the "**Add Message number to Subject Line**" option. See **Figure 3-12**.

Once defined, the next time a new message is created, *Outpost* automatically places a message identifier in the subject line, and the user can enter additional subject line text following the identifier. The message number automatically increments to the next number ensuring unique messages from this station.

Policy #4: Keep Messages As Short As Possible

This is another common sense policy that should be obvious. This is even more critical if there are a large number of stations competing for bandwidth at 1200 baud.

Implementing this packet policy is may a matter of what you won't do instead of what you could do. For instance:

Outpost supports placing a signature on a message form. These signatures should be for key-stroke convenience, and not to state titles, addresses, phone numbers, and other information that may be irrelevant during a disaster.

When replying to or forwarding a message, *Outpost* puts a copy of the original message in the new message. While this is a nice feature during non-emergency times and with traditional high-speed e-mail, it could burden a message with text that does not add any value. It is recommended that if you do reply to or forward a message, review it for relevance, and trim the text as necessary.

Lastly, how long should a message be? It should be long enough to convey the intent of the sender, and not a character longer. In short, avoid general wordiness.

Policy #5: Frequency Of Polling The BBS

Creating efficient messages, as described above, is one way to manage the frequency. The other means is to manage how often you poll the BBS for incoming messages. It needs to be understood that there is overhead with checking for a message on the BBS. You issue the connect request, receive the BBS header, execute the List Mine (LM) command, execute the List Bulletins (LB) command, receive the list of bulletins (hoping that there is a new one you didn't already retrieve), then disconnect. With no other traffic this could be less than 1 minute of connect time. However, if everyone is constantly polling the BBS, it is likely that only the station with the loudest signal will get all the attention.

Outpost offers two methods for automatically polling the BBS to send and receive messages (**Tools > Send/Receive Settings**). See **Figure 3-13**. The user can selects the number of minutes that they want *Outpost* to initiate a Send/Receive Session. The range of interval times is from 1 to 999 minutes (about 16 and a half hours).

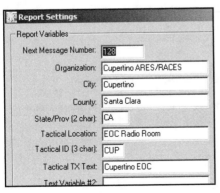

Figure 3-12—Outpost can create a concatenated unique message identifier based on the 3 character *Tactical ID* and the *Next Message Number*, both defined from the Tools > Reports Settings Menu.

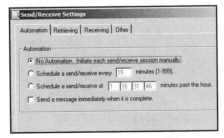

Figure 3-13—Outpost offers two methods for automatically polling the BBS to send and receive messages (Tools > Send/Receive Settings).

The user can also select up to 4 absolute times during the 60 minutes of an hour when *Outpost* will run. This approach essentially allows "slots" of BBS access to be assigned to a number of *Outpost* users within a packet network. It is best used when a group of *Outpost* users operating on the same frequency need access to the same BBS and they work together to pick their individual slot times. If designed correctly, Slot Timing should significantly reduce the amount of collisions between competing packet stations.

Policy #6: Polling For Message Types

Another way of reducing unnecessary traffic is to carefully poll for only the types of message that are relevant to the disaster. In most cases, packet message traffic is made up on private messages sent from one station intended for another. However, there are times when bulletins are good, and the need to send a broadcast message to packet installations is critical.

Minimally, you should plan to retrieve messages addressed to you (Private Messages, **Tools > Send/Receive Settings**). If packet NTS messages are also passed, check this box as well.

However, retrieving bulletins depends on the BBS that you are using. If the BBS is dedicated to your ARES/RACES operations *and* not connected to the global packet network *and* your organization plans to send bulletins, then check the option **Retrieve New Bulletins**. All new bulletins not previously downloaded will be retrieved. (**Figure 3-14**.)

If your BBS is open to the public AND is connected to the global packet network, then check the option **Retrieve Selected Bulletins**. However, to use this approach, the Emergency Communications Team needs to agree on an addressing scheme that allows *Outpost* users to poll for only those bulletins of interest among the hundreds of thousands that are up on the BBS.

For instance, suppose your ARES/RACES organization plans to send bulletins to all County sites, all fire base camps, all staging areas, and provide general weather updates. They may define addresses as ALLCTY, ALFIRE, ALSTAG,

and WX. In *Outpost*, check the option **Retrieve Selected Bulletins**, and enter these addresses in the Filter fields.

Policy #7: Packet Messages Are Part Of The Official Record

As the saying goes, the job is not done until the paperwork is complete. Regardless of the disaster, two things are true: an affected municipality wants to speed the recovery regardless of what is required, and they want to recover their costs. For instance, California uses the Standardized Emergency Management System (SEMS) for managing emergencies that involve multiple jurisdictions or agencies. SEMS requires emergency response agencies to use the Incident Command System (ICS) as the basis emergency management system.

One of the ICS functions is Finance/Administration. They have the job to track all financial and cost aspects of the incident with, among other things, an eye on submitting expenses for reimbursement. To back up reimbursement requests, all event documentation – logs, forms, receipts, check-lists, and message forms – is collected as part of the official record and the appropriate documentation is submitted as support for a reimbursement request. Packet messages become part of this record.

Packet messages managed in *Outpost* can be submitted a couple of different ways:

- Print a message. *Outpost* lets you print a message to a printer one at a time. This approach is recommended if your municipality or agency requires specific paper copies of messages to be submitted at the close of the event.

- Save-All File. *Outpost* allows you to save all messages associated with a folder to a file. The contents of this file are printer-ready and include page breaks between messages. This approach is recommended if your municipality or agency requires all messages printed at the close of the event, or will accept an electronic version of the messages with the intent of printing them at a later date if needed.

- *Outpost* Archive File. This file is created by exporting messages from one or all *Outpost* folders to a file that could be imported again at a later time. This approach is recommended only to recreate an actual trail of messages generated within *Outpost*.

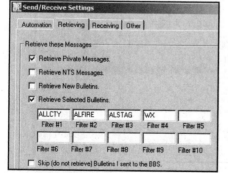

Figure 3-14—Retrieving bulletins depends on the BBS that you are using. If the BBS is dedicated to your ARES/RACES operations and not connected to the global packet network and your organization plans to send bulletins, then check the option Retrieve New Bulletins. All new bulletins not previously downloaded will be retrieved.

Passing Effective Messages

Emergency communications response teams use packet radio primarily for moving messages that do not lend themselves very well to being passed as voice traffic. Typical information that is ideal for packet includes (but definitely not limited to):

■ A request list of shelter supplies
■ Descriptions of medicines, pharmaceuticals, chemicals, or anything complex where the exact spelling is critical
■ Detailed instructions, directions, or process steps
■ Structured data that needs to be rolled up at the receiving end
■ Common formatted status reports, or other types of agency reports

Because users can send (and BBSs can store) messages consisting of ASCII characters, it is possible for an *Outpost* user to send information from a wide range of applications that store their data in ASCII. While packet is ideal for sharing lists of materials, requests, or resources is perfect for packet, spreadsheets are perfect for managing the lists. To give you a sense on how to integrate these two programs, the following shows how *Outpost* can easily work with Microsoft's *Excel* spreadsheet program (note that other spreadsheet programs essentially behave the same).

A spreadsheet allows you to store either data in individual cells. Sometimes, formulas are used to calculate a data value from one or more cells. Regardless on how the data is derived, it can be extracted from a spreadsheet and copied into an *Outpost* message. The easiest method is to copy the cells you want to send, then paste them into an *Outpost* message form.

For this example, let's assume you are operating out of a shelter and it needs a list of material to be delivered from the regional Red Cross Material Replenishment Center.

The shelter manager has directed his logistics lead to use a spreadsheet to track what supplies the shelter has and the items that they need. A sample spreadsheet could look like the one shown in **Figure 3-15**.

The logistics lead passes off a copy of the spreadsheet to you and asks that the first 16 rows be sent to the replenishment center. After opening the spreadsheet, you highlight the data to be sent, select Edit->Copy from the spreadsheet menu (or press **CNTL-C**) to copy the message to the *Windows* clipboard.

Back at *Outpost*, you open an *Outpost* message form, position the cursor in the message area, and select Edit->Paste (or press **CNTL-V**). The text Add whatever additional message text as required. (**Figure 3-16**.)

As you look at the message form, you will see that the data is not always aligned to the column as it was displayed in the spreadsheet. This is because when *Windows* takes the copy from the spreadsheet, it separates the data in a row using a TAB character. These TAB characters nicely keep the data separate as it is sent over packet.

If the information is to be imported into a spreadsheet at the receiving station, *do not change the spacing between the data items*. This will misalign the data during the recovery process at the receiving station (this process relies on one TAB character between each column data entry).

If the information is to be only viewed or printed at the receiving station, you can "clean up" the look of the message by entering additional tabs to re-align the data to columns. Press **CNTL-TAB** to enter tabs into the message window. When done, press Send to move the message in the Out Tray, then Send/Receive to send the message on its way.

At the receiving station, let's assume the above received

	A	B	C	D	E	F
1	Shelter:	Quinlan				
2	City:	Cupertino, CA				
3	Request:	Material Replenishment				
4	Date:	8/15/2007				
5						
6	Item No	Description	On Hand	U/E	Qty needed	When Needed
7	1	Cots	30	ea	25	16-Aug-07
8	2	Blankets	45	ea	15	16-Aug-07
9	3	water, 12 oz bottles	200	bottles	150	18-Aug-07
10	4	First Aid kits	3	kits	12	16-Aug-07
11	5	toilet paper	50	rolls	250	16-Aug-07
12	6	tooth brushes	10	ea	50	16-Aug-07
13	7	tooth paste	5	ea	55	16-Aug-07
14	8	note pads	0	ea	25	16-Aug-07
15	9	pencils	0	ea	25	16-Aug-07
16	10	MRE	10	servings	300	16-Aug-07
17						

Figure 3-15—A sample *Excel* spreadsheet from a shelter manager.

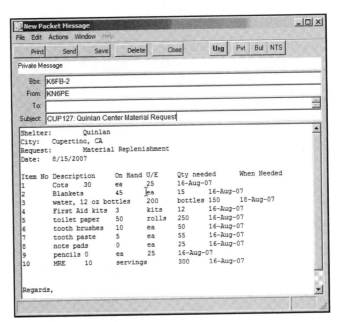

Figure 3-16—Sending the shelter spreadsheet via Outpost.

data is to be imported into a new spreadsheet. Once the *Outpost* message arrives, open the message, highlight the data that was sent, and either press **CNTL-C** or **Edit->Copy** from the message menu.

Open the spreadsheet; position the cursor in the upper-right cell where the data will be inserted, and press **CNTL-V**, or **Edit-> Paste**. Save the spreadsheet, and deliver the file to the intended user.

Of course, at the receiving end the formatting is not preserved when compared to the source spreadsheet. In this kind of ASCII spreadsheet data transfer, formatting that will be lost includes the bold cells, column width spacing, line drawing, position alignment within the cell (left, right, or centered), and any cell formulas. Keep in mind that we didn't send a formatted spreadsheet, just the data.

One decision that Operational Area Responders should make is how data should be passed and in what format. Resolving this question up front whether the data will be printed or imported into another application will reduce the amount of data reformatting later on.

D-STAR

The D-STAR digital protocol was born in 2001 as a project funded by the Japanese Ministry of Posts and Telecommunications to investigate digital technologies for Amateur Radio. The research committee included representatives of Japanese Amateur Radio manufacturers, including ICOM, and the Japan Amateur Radio League (JARL). The JARL is the publisher of the D-STAR protocol (a technical description is included in the appendix of this book)

All radio manufacturers are free to develop D-STAR equipment, but at the time of this writing ICOM is the only company that has done so for the US amateur market. Because of this fact, amateurs tend to associate the D-STAR digital protocol with the ICOM Corporation. Although ICOM may develop D-STAR protocol enhancements peculiar to the function of its hardware, ICOM does not "own" the original D-STAR protocol.

WHAT IS D-STAR?

Another misconception about D-STAR is that it is strictly a digital voice protocol. The primary application of D-STAR is indeed voice, but it is a system capable of handling any sort of data—text, voice, images, etc.

As shown in **Figure 4-1**, a D-STAR network can take several forms. D-STAR compatible transceivers can communicate directly (simplex), or through a D-STAR repeater for wide coverage. It is important to note that D-STAR signals cannot be repeated through traditional analog repeaters.

D-STAR repeaters, in turn, can link together to form a backbone. This linking can take place with RF (microwave) or by way of the Internet.

The D-STAR system carries

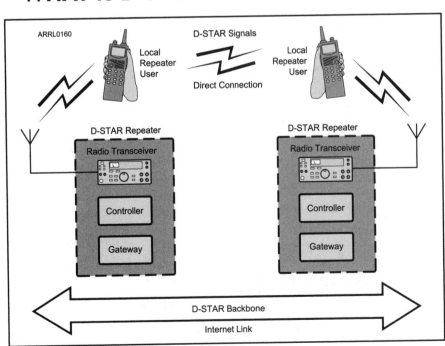

Figure 4-1—A D-STAR network can take several forms. D-STAR compatible transceivers can communicate directly (simplex) or through a D-STAR repeater for wide coverage.

digitized voice and digital data, but does the job in two different ways. There is a combined voice-and-data mode (DV) and a high-speed data-only stream (DD). From the perspective of the D-STAR user, data and voice are carried at different rates and managed in different ways, but over the air, they are transported in *packets*.

Digital Voice and Low-Speed Data (DV)

D-STAR digitizes analog voice by using the AMBE 2020 codec. AMBE stands for Advanced Multiple Band Encoding and 2020 designates the particular variation used by D-STAR. (Detailed technical information about AMBE 2020 is available at **www.dvsinc.com/products/a2020.htm**).

AMBE can digitize voice at several different rates. The D-STAR system uses a 2.4k bits per second (bps) rate that offers a good compromise between intelligibility and the speed at which data must be transmitted via the radio link. In addition, AMBE adds information to the voice data that allows the receiving codec to correct errors introduced during transmission. The net result is that the digitized voice stream carries data at a rate of 3.6 kbps.

Low-Speed Data

Along with the digitized voice information, D-STAR's DV mode can also carry 8-bit digital data at 1200 bps.

Radios that support DV voice and data present an RS-232 or USB 1.1 interface to the user as shown in **Figure 4-2**. (The RS-232 interface is restricted to RxD, TxD, and ground--"three-wire" connection.) Any computer terminal or program that can exchange data over those types of interfaces can use D-STAR's DV mode capabilities as a "radio cable."

Because D-STAR's DV mode handles the data stream in an unmodified "raw" format, it is up to the equipment or programs that are exchanging data to manage its flow. For example, if one system is busy and can't accept data, it must be able to signal the sending system to stop sending

data and then start again when ready again. This process is called *flow control*. D-STAR requires the sender and receiver to perform flow control by using special data characters. This is called *software flow control*.

High-Speed Data (DD)

D-STAR's high-speed data mode is called *D-STAR DD*. Unlike DV, this mode does transmit voice data simultaneously. The data-only packets sent over the RF link at a raw data rate of 128k bps, but since that includes the packet header and the delay between packets, the *net data rate* is somewhat lower. As with the DV mode, data is transmitted without modification so flow control is left to the users on each end. Radios supporting DD mode communications may also support DV mode.

Users connect to a radio supporting DD mode with an Ethernet interface via the usual RJ-45 modular jack found on computer networking equipment. The DD mode interface looks to computer equipment just like a customary network connection. Specifically, the DD mode interface is an Ethernet "bridge" between a pair of fixed network addresses. This allows Web browsers and other Internet software to run normally, as if they were connected to standard computer network.

The net data rate of DD mode is comparable to or better than a high-speed dial-up Internet connection. Voice transmission using DD mode connections can be accomplished digitizing the voice separately and transmitting it as a stream of data via D-STAR. (Since DD mode just treats the digitized voice as data, any codec may be used.) Any streaming media mode that will run over dial-up Internet will likely perform well over D-STAR, too.

With its high signaling rate at 130-kHz bandwidth, FCC regulations restrict D-STAR DD operating to the 902 MHz and higher bands.

D-STAR Backbone

As we discussed earlier, D-STAR backbones are used to link individual D-STAR repeaters. Backbone connections can be made by any combination of Internet (a broadband connection is required at the repeater site) or radio links. Users cannot access a D-STAR backbone directly; it is used only by the D-STAR repeater gateways.

Gateways communicate over the D-STAR backbone using the Asynchronous Transfer Mode (ATM) protocol. The backbone operates at data rates of up to 10 Mbps, depending on the connection available. If the radio

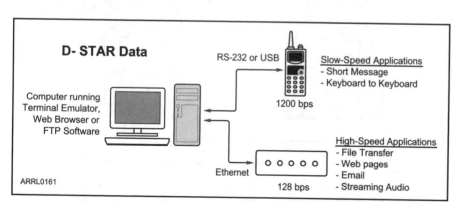

Figure 4-2— Radios that support DV voice and data present an RS-232 or USB 1.1 interface to the user.

link backbone is used, signal bandwidth can be as high at 10.5 MHz, so these links are restricted to the amateur microwave bands. (ICOM currently provides a 10.7 GHz microwave point-to-point radio link.)

It is worth noting that while D-STAR is an open protocol, ICOM's implementation of Internet gateway functionality is accomplished through proprietary ICOM software.

WHAT D-STAR IS NOT

It is important to understand what D-STAR systems can not or may not do, due to both technical and regulatory restrictions.

D-STAR uses many techniques that are derived from or seem similar to those of the mobile phone systems and the Internet. Nevertheless, D-STAR does not create a "Ham Radio Cell Phone" or an "Amateur Internet." Most importantly, D-STAR communications are public and can be monitored by anyone with a D-STAR radio or a receiver capable of decoding D-STAR signals.

Streaming media are also quite constrained by D-STAR's limited data rate. Anyone expecting to watch video or download music via a D-STAR DD mode connection will likely be disappointed. D-STAR supports reasonable

amateur requirements, but is not a replacement for broadband Internet connections.

The intent of D-STAR is to provide amateurs with state-of-the-art digital communications to support traditional amateur communications and foster the development of new applications suitable for amateur radio.

Hams using D-STAR's DD mode can certainly connect to the Internet, send and receive e-mail, use FTP servers, and so forth. Nevertheless, the FCC's prohibition against using Amateur Radio for commercial purposes still applies. This means that D-STAR users and system owners must be vigilant in keeping the many commercial aspects of the Internet off of the D-STAR system.

D-STAR PROTOCOL—THE NITTY GRITTY

D-STAR is a packet-based protocol, which means the data is assembled into packages containing the data itself plus other information about the data and how the communications system should handle it. Packets are transmitted in their entirety and the receiving system processes the packets as a group.

There are two types of packets in the D-STAR radio link protocol; DV (data and voice) and DD (high-speed data). **Figure 4-3** shows the basic structure of each type of packet. Before examining the details, observe the similarities between the two packets. The packets consist of a *header* segment and a *data* segment. (Data segments are sometimes referred to as *payloads*.)

The header segment contains information about the packet; control *flags*, identification of the sender and destination, and D-STAR network routing directions. The header contains the information the receiving device needs to process the data, whether that means reading and acting on the data or just forwarding it on to another receiver elsewhere in the system.

The D-STAR backbone has its own protocol that carries the gateway-to-gateway information — the Asynchronous Transfer Mode (ATM) protocol. Because the method by which the gateways communicate is not public, the ATM protocol is not discussed in this course.

Overhead

The header and other information added to the original set of data creates a small amount of *packet overhead*. The additional information in the header is transmitted at the same rate as the data, reducing the net data rate. It is

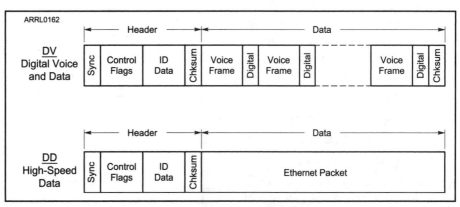

Figure 4-3—The basic structure of each type of D-STAR packet.

Table 4-1

D-STAR Protocol Overhead

Protocol	Header (bytes)[1]	Data (bytes)	Packet Size (bytes)	Overhead Bytes	Pct (%)
DV	51	1056	1107	51	4.6
DD (min data)[2]	51	66	117	51	43.5
DD (max data)[2]	51	1520	1571	51	3.2

[1]The header size is rounded up to the next full byte because of the 15-bit sync field.
[2]Data size includes the terminating checksum.

a challenge for protocol designers to minimize overhead, while still providing enough information to make the protocol useful.

Table 4-1 shows the amount of overhead for the DV and DD packets. The DV packets are always the same size with 11 pairs of voice and data frames.

Protocol Overhead Differences

An important difference between packet radio and D-STAR is that packet radio (AX.25) requires an acknowledgement and the receiver can request retransmission if the packet is received with errors. The time it takes for the packet's receiver to process and acknowledge the packet adds to the overall time to transfer data. This waiting time is called *protocol overhead*. D-STAR is a one-way protocol--no response is required from the receiver to acknowledge that a packet was received. D-STAR does not require acknowledgement because error detection and correction are built-in to the data.

Encapsulation

D-STAR also employs a common technique of using one protocol to send data formatted according to another protocol. In the DV packet, voice data is contained in short segments (called *frames*) formatted according to the AMBE protocol. In the DD packet, the data segment is formatted according to the Ethernet protocol. This process of putting data from one protocol "inside" another protocol is called *encapsulation*. The encapsulating protocol (D-STAR in this case) acts as a wrapper or envelope for the packets from the encapsulated protocol, just as a paper envelope carries documents or letters.

D-STAR Packet Structure

Each D-STAR packet consists of specific components, not unlike AX.25 packets. Let's take a quick look at each one.

Header: The header segment is the same for both the DV and DD packets. **Figure 4-4** shows the structure of the D-STAR packet header.

Sync Frames: Because a packet can start at any time, it takes the receiver some time to detect and synchronize with the incoming packet data. Sync frames are unique patterns of bits that the receiver can use to unambiguously determine that a packet is beginning. The receiver is then ready to process the data elements that follow. D-STAR uses two sync frames. Bit Sync is a standard pattern for the GMSK 1010 modulation used by D-STAR. Frame Sync is '111011001010000' - a unique bit pattern in D-STAR packets.

Control Flags: The bits in the control flag bytes are used to direct the processing of the packet. For a detailed description of the function of each bit, refer to the D-STAR protocol technical description document.

Flag 1: Flag 1 bits indicate whether the data is control data or user data, whether communications is simplex or repeater, set priority, etc.

Flag 2: Flag 2 is reserved for future use as identification data.

Flag 3: Flag 3 is reserved to indicate the version of the D-STAR protocol being used so that if new functions are added in the future, the receiver can apply them properly.

Identification Data: There are four *fields* of identification data. These carry information about the origin and

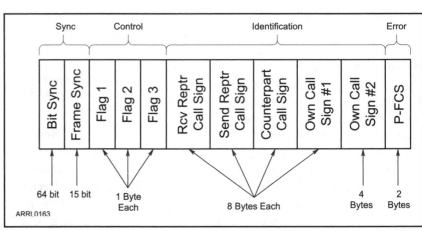

Figure 4-4—The structure of the D-STAR packet header.

destination of the packet.

Receive Repeater Call Sign: The call sign of the repeater that is to receive the packet

Send Repeater Call Sign: The call sign of the repeater that is sending the packet

Counterpart Call Sign: The call sign of the station that is to receive the data.

Own Call Sign #1 and Own Call Sign #2: The first field contains the call sign of the station that originated the data. The second field contains suffix information.

P-FCS Checksum: A *checksum* is used to detect errors as described below. The P-FCS checksum is computed from the Flag and ID data bytes. Any transmission errors in those bytes can be detected as a discrepancy in the P-FCS value.

D-STAR Error Detection and Correction

Transmission errors can occur in any digital data transmission, even those over wired networks. Somewhere along the way, a noise burst or a loose connection changes whatever represents a 0 bit to a 1 bit or vice versa. Depend-

ing on the bit's importance, the result can be insignificant or catastrophic.

To combat transmission errors, D-STAR uses two techniques:

Error detection codes are used to detect transmission errors. These only tell the receiver that the data is damaged, but not how. D-STAR checksums follow the CRC-CCITT standard.

Error correcting codes contain information about the payload data. Because the codes are sent with the data to enable correction at the receiver, they are called *Forward Error Correcting* or FEC codes. FEC codes contain enough extra information for the receiver to repair most damage.

Both the DV and DD data packets use the P_FCS checksum to protect the information in the header. The DD data packet also contains the Ethernet data packet checksum at the very end of the packet. It protects the Ethernet data payload.

In the DV packet data segment, each AMBE 2020 digitized voice frame contains its own FEC code to allow the receiver to repair errors in that 20 msec of speech. DV digital data frames are not protected, relying on the transmitting and receiving applications to detect and correct errors.

D-STAR NETWORKING

D-STAR packets contain call signs identifying the origin and destination of each transmission, as well as repeater stations through which the transmission is routed. Call signs are stored in the memories of each D-STAR transmitter, just as alphanumeric labels can be stored in many modern VHF/UHF transmitters.

As you may recall from the previous discussion, each D-STAR header packet can carry up to four different call signs. The following list begins with the name of the field in the D-STAR packet (see **Figure 4-5**) for each of the four call signs:

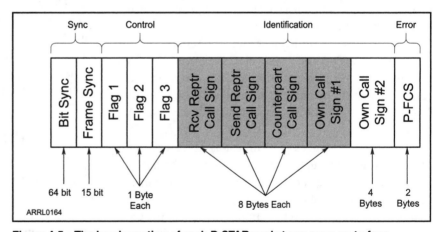

Figure 4-5—The header potion of each D-STAR packet can carry up to four different call signs. Own Call Sign #2 isn't counted because it only contains suffix information.

Own Call Sign — the call sign of the user making the transmission, referred to as "my call sign". Although Own Call Sign #2 is a separate field, it carries only suffix information, not a whole call sign.

Counterpart Call Sign — the call sign of the station the user is in contact with, referred to as "your call sign" or "UR."

Sender Repeater Call Sign — the repeater and specific module (A-D) through which the user intends to communicate, referred to as "repeater 1."

Receiver Repeater Call Sign — the repeater and specific module (A-D) through which the station identified by Counterpart Call Sign will communicate, referred to as "repeater 2."

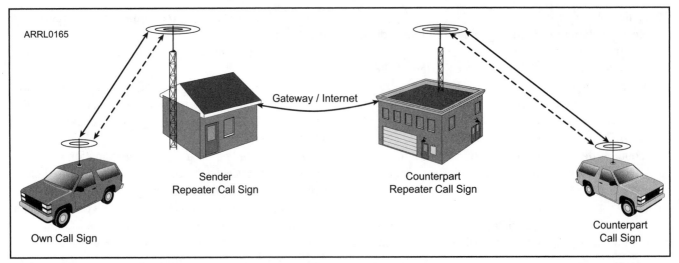

Figure 4-6—The call signs provide the identity of the packet's origin, destination and repeaters used. The D-STAR network needs this information to make sure that the packets from one station to another take the right path.

The call signs provide the identity of the packet's origin, destination, and repeaters used. The D-STAR network needs this information to make sure that the packets from one station to another take the right path as illustrated in **Figure 4-6**. The repeaters can be located anywhere there is Internet access, so the users can be across town or on different continents.

Each D-STAR repeater can have up to four *modules* that handle voice or data, each identified by a letter; A, B, C or D. Each module acts as a separate repeater sharing a common controller with the other modules. By adding the module identifier letter in a repeater call sign, the information is routed only to that module.

It is important to remember that even though a transmission may be directed to a specific station, all D-STAR transmissions not over an Internet link are public and can be monitored by anyone, just as on analog repeaters. There are no "private conversations" on the D-STAR network.

D-STAR recognizes government-assigned call signs of users or repeaters up to 8 characters long, which is sufficient for a 6-character call, plus a slash and one numeric portable indicator digit. Extra information can be added as a suffix to the originating station's call sign in the Own Call Sign #2 field.

Note that any routing suffix letters must be in the 8th available space in the call sign. For example, if the repeater has a 4-character call sign, three spaces must be added before the routing suffix letter.

If the character string "CQCQCQ" is present in the Counterpart Call Sign field, it indicates that the calling station wishes to talk to any station. This is the same as saying "N9JA monitoring" or "W7JRL for a contact" on an analog repeater.

Prefixes and Suffixes

Prefixes and suffixes added to the call sign do not have the same meaning or format as in an analog transmission. These prefixes and suffixes are routing information for the D-STAR repeater controllers to tell them how to handle the packet. D-STAR suffix characters are separated from the call by spaces.

Point-to-Point Simplex

The simplest D-STAR contact is a simplex, user-to-user contact without any repeaters involved. To make a simplex contact, the calling station programs their call sign in the Own Call Sign field and "CQCQCQ" or the desired station's call sign in the Counterpoint Call Sign field. Operation is then conducted just as it is on analog FM.

Repeater Operation

Using a local D-STAR repeater is very much like simplex communications except that the repeater's call sign must be programmed into the Sender Repeater Call Sign field. For a repeater to relay a D-STAR signal, it must recognize its own call sign in the packets from the transmitting station. The transmitting station must also include the letter identifying the repeater module being used in the repeater call sign.

D-STAR Zones

Just as analog repeaters can be linked together to extend the range of communications, D-STAR repeater modules can be linked into *zones*. A D-STAR Zone consists of all of the repeater modules that share a

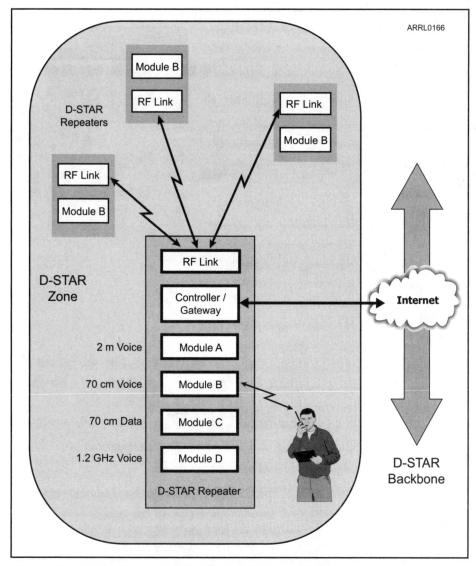

D-STAR repeaters around the world. Using a gateway is how users in different zones can communicate. The user is required to know the call sign of the zone's repeater that provides the gateway.

Adding a "G" to a repeater call tells the D-STAR repeaters to send the transmission via the gateway. Note that the "G" must be in the 8th available space in the call sign, so if the repeater has a 4-character call sign, three spaces must be added before the "G."

Call Routing

What if the user does not know the call sign of the repeater on which the desired station is operating? The D-STAR network provides that information automatically through the D-STAR *registry*.

The registry is a database of user call signs registered on the D-STAR network by repeater system operators. Each D-STAR gateway has a copy of that database, which is maintained by several D-STAR *trusted servers* located around the world. Each D-STAR repeater gateway database is updated a number of times each day.

Figure 4-7— A D-STAR Zone consists of all of the repeater modules that share a common gateway, the Internet connection for a D-STAR repeater. A D-STAR backbone can also be an RF-only connection.

common *gateway*, the RF backbone or Internet connection for a D-STAR repeater. **Figure 4-7** shows how this works.

Within the group of repeaters, modules identified with the same letter, such as "B", form a D-STAR Zone. The zone may be a single repeater with a single module assigned the letter B or there may be several repeaters with B modules. The important thing to remember is that all of the repeaters must share a single, common gateway.

D-STAR Internet Gateway

A D-STAR Internet gateway is a broadband Internet connection from a D-STAR repeater controller to other

For a user to make use of the D-STAR network, his or her call sign must be added to the registry by a D-STAR repeater operator, just as you are assigned a password for a computer system. (Note that you can make simplex contacts without registering.) Once added to the list, each time the user transmits via a D-STAR repeater, the user's location is updated in the master registry where it will be provided to all D-STAR gateways.

To contact a registered station, the calling station enters that call sign into the UR call sign field and instructs the repeater to use the gateway by adding "G" after the R1 or R2 call sign as described above. The D-STAR controller will then look up the station's call in its database and route the call to the repeater on which the call last registered.

D-STAR RADIOS

Remember that D-STAR is an open protocol and available to any manufacturer. At the time this book went to press, however, ICOM is the only manufacturer offering D-STAR compatible radios and repeaters. So, by default, the focus of any discussion of D-STAR hardware has to center on ICOM gear.

An ICOM ID-1 transceiver.

To determine which is the best radio for an application, the first step is to understand what the requirements are:

■ Is DD mode operation required (high-speed data)? If so, the only radio supporting DD mode is the ICOM ID-1.
■ Is dual-band operation required?
■ Is high-power required?
■ If data is to be transmitted, what data interface does the computer have?

When adding up the costs, don't forget to include the ICOM UT-118 D-STAR module if the radio requires one for digital operation.

Key items to remember when choosing the right D-STAR technology:

■ High-speed data (DD mode) can only be sent on the bands above 70 cm.
■ Error correction for low-speed data (DV mode) is the responsibility of the data communications programs used to exchange data.
■ RS-232 interfaces for D-STAR data do not provide data flow control hardware signals, such as RTS or CTS, but XON/XOFF software flow control is provided.
■ Higher power radios will result in stronger signal strengths and fewer data transmission errors.
■ If data is to be transmitted while in motion, higher frequencies will result in fewer transmission errors, improving the net data exchange rate.

ARRL0167

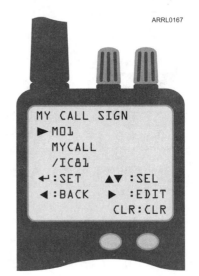

Figure 4-8—The result of programming "MYCALL/IC91" into the first (M01) memory for MY CALL SIGN.

Configuring an ICOM D-STAR Radio

D-STAR radios may all have slightly different labels, keys, and sequences of operation, but under the surface they all use the same sets of D-STAR information. By studying the ICOM IC-91AD configuration process, you'll be able to quickly learn to configure other D-STAR radios. (The IC-91AD manual can be downloaded from ICOM at **icomamerica.com/downloads/manuals.asp**.) The same techniques also apply to the newer IC-92AD.

Call Signs

The most important D-STAR information is your own call sign. The IC-91AD stores this information labeled as MY CALL SIGN.\
■ Select MENU
■ Select CALL SIGN

ARRL0168

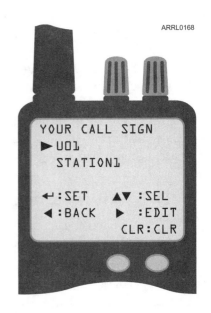

Figure 4-9— "STATION1" programmed into memory U01.

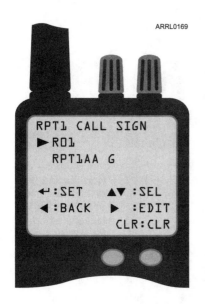

```
RPT1 CALL SIGN
► R01
  RPT1AA G

↵:SET      ▲▼ :SEL
◄ :BACK    ► :EDIT
           CLR:CLR
```

Figure 4-10—
"RPT1AA G"
programmed into
memory R01.

- Select MY
- Select which of the MY CALL SIGN memories (M01-M06) is to be programmed (the IC-91AD can store up to six different call signs)
- Enter up to 8 characters
- If a suffix is desired, select the "/" character and then follow it with up to 4 characters.
- Exit the MENU system

Figure 4-8 shows the result of programming "MY-CALL/IC91" into the first (M01) memory for MY CALL SIGN. You might want multiple selections for MY CALL SIGN if the radio is shared by more than one operator or if you frequently operate away from home or with a club call sign.

Along with your own call, D-STAR's ability to call other system users directly by call sign means you'll want to set up a list of commonly contacted call signs. The IC-91AD labels these calls "YOUR CALL SIGN" and can store up to 60 8-character call signs in memories U-1-U60. The process of accessing and entering the data is similar to that for "MY CALL SIGN", selecting "UR" instead of "MY." **Figure 4-9** shows "STATION1" programmed into memory U01.

The D-STAR repeater call signs are part of establishing a D-STAR connection, so the IC-91AD can also store 60 8-character call signs for repeaters in memories R01-R60. These are labeled "RPT1/2 CALL SIGN". **Figure 4-10** shows "RPT1AA G" programmed into memory R01. You can store several variations of repeater call signs to make local calls ("RPT1AA") or zone calls ("/RPT1AA") through the same

repeater without having to manually edit the call sign each time.

Useful Functions

D-STAR radios can also take advantage of the information contained in each packet to provide handy functions, such as automatically loading received call signs and repeater routing. Each of these IC-91AD functions can be enabled or disabled as part of the radio configuration. Other radios may provide a different set of configuration options.

AUTO REPLY - a method of replying with a pre-recorded voice message

BREAK IN - allows you to enter a conversation if the stations are using CALL SIGN SQUELCH (see next item)

CALL SIGN SQUELCH - mutes the receiver output audio unless packets addressed to MY CALL SIGN are received

EMR - enables full audio output whenever an EMR call is received

RX CALL SIGN AUTO WRITE - temporarily acquires and stores the call sign of the calling station

RPT CALL SIGN AUTO WRITE - temporarily acquires and stores the call sign of the repeaters used by the calling station

Operating an ICOM D-STAR Radio

As you have seen, configuring your radio to take advantage of the information stored in the D-STAR packets can make operating much simpler. Assuming that it's configured to use these "smart call" features, here's how to use the IC-91AD for common tasks.

The ICOM ID-1 transceiver shown without its removable control head.

Frequency Selection

There is nothing special about frequency selection on D-STAR radios--in VFO mode, just turn the VFO knob! You can store frequencies (including repeater offsets) in memory channels for later recall just on an analog radio.

Monitoring

The squelch function of digital radios does not function the same way as for an analog radio. DV mode offers the option of *CSS (Call Sign Squelch)* in which the radio remains silent until D-STAR packets are received containing the specified call sign. Selecting "no squelch" means that you will hear every signal that can be decoded from D-STAR packets. You can then monitor all conversations on the channel — there are no private contacts!

Calling CQ

First, select your simplex or repeater frequency as described above. Then select either of these two methods:
- Store "CQCQCQ" in one of the memories from U01 to U60 and retrieve it.
- Press and hold the "0 CQ" key to load "CQCQCQ" into YOUR CALL SIGN.

By setting YOUR CALL SIGN to "CQCQCQ" you can make transmissions that are not intended for a specific station, such as announcements, test transmissions, or soliciting a contact.

Getting an Answer

When you get an answer, the display of the radio will show you the call sign of the station calling and you can also view the repeater or repeaters used in the D-STAR network.

Store the caller's call sign in YOUR CALL SIGN by pressing the CALL/RX>CS key. This also stores the R1 and R2 (if present) call signs. Talk to the calling station as you would normally.

Your radio will also have functions to transfer the temporarily saved station and repeater call signs to long-term memory channels.

Text Messaging

D-STAR also supports the exchange of short text messages, similar to Internet Messaging (IM) or a mobile phone's Short Messaging Service (SMS). The IC-91AD allows the operator to make up messages or store and retrieve them from message memories. (The IC-91AD has 6 message channels, CH01-CH06, of 20 characters each.)
- Select MENU
- Select MESSAGE / POSITION
- Select TX MESSAGE

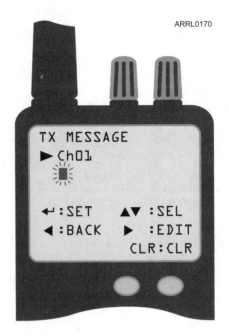

Figure 4-11—
Now the IC-91AD is ready for an operator to input text characters for text message memory CH01.

- Select which of the message memories (CH01-CH06) is to be programmed or edited
- A stored message may be edited at this point
- To store the message, press the "5" key to store the message.

The message will then be included in the header of the D-STAR packet on all transmissions under text messaging is turned OFF.

Figure 4-11 shows the IC-91AD ready for an operator to input text characters for text message memory CH01.

Data Transmission

There are two ways to send data in the DV mode; PTT and AUTO. (The transmission mode is a configurable item that is selected via the menu system.)

PTT mode does not transmit until the PTT switch is closed on the radio or at the microphone jack (either by a microphone or an external circuit). While PTT is closed, the radio transmits whatever data it receives.

AUTO mode transmits data as it is sent to the data interface. The communications software used to generate and receive data should be set to:
- **Specified by the radio** — this is the speed of the data between the software host and the radio, not across the D-STAR link!

8 data bits

1 stop bit

No parity bit
- **Software flow control** — XON/XOFF between the radio and computer

LOCAL D-STAR OPERATION

The vast majority of time "on channel" is spent just listening or monitoring. Monitoring works just the same on D-STAR as it does for analog FM. You do not have to enter any call signs for the radio to receive D-STAR packets. Once your radio is tuned to an active channel frequency, you'll hear every conversation. The only difference is the squelch function.

The squelch function of digital radios does not function the same way as for an analog radio. Instead of "opening" the squelch to hear unmodulated white noise, your radio is silent until D-STAR packets are received, then the decoded digital voice will be heard over the speaker as long as the signal is strong enough to receive the packets properly.

If D-STAR's DV mode is in use, the CSS (Call Sign Squelch) is available. When CSS is turned ON and a call sign entered, the radio will remain silent until D-STAR packets containing the specified call sign are received. Since the transmitting station's call sign is contained in every D-STAR packet, CSS does away with having to agree on a special code as with analog Digitally Coded Squelch where tone sequences are transmitted.

Along with speech, D-STAR data and digital messages can also be received and displayed by a listener. All digital information is carried by the D-STAR packet as "plain text."

UR - CQCQCQ
R1 - blank
R2 - blank
MY - W7JRL

W7JRL

N5MIJ

N9JA

Figure 4-12— This string can be stored in a call sign memory, just like regular call signs. Some radios will even have a "CQ" key to set YOUR CALL SIGN to "CQCQCQ" automatically.

Making a Call & Responding

What if your transmissions are not directed specifically at another station? There are many instances in which you might want to simply have everyone listening hear your voice. Of course, the most common example is announcing that you are listening yourself and are available for a contact - "This is N9JA, monitoring." At other times, you might want to make an announcement about traffic conditions or as a net control station, make frequent transmissions to manage net functions.

In cases like this, you would not enter another station's call sign as YOUR CALL SIGN, nor would you leave it empty. D-STAR's solution is to use the special text string "CQCQCQ" as seen in **Figure 4-12**. This string can be stored in a call sign memory, just like regular call signs. Some radios will even have a "CQ" key to set YOUR CALL SIGN to "CQCQCQ" automatically.

It's worth noting that if MY CALL SIGN is set to your call sign, any transmission that you make will be identified in the D-STAR packet header. However, it is good amateur practice to announce your call sign by voice as well.

Here's how to enter the call signs in a D-STAR radio for a simplex contact using the IC-91AD call sign entry labels; UR, R1, R2, and MY:

Calling CQ (Calling Station)
UR: CQCQCQ
R1: Blank
R2: Blank
MY: [calling station's call sign]

Responding to a CQ and during the QSO (Responding Station)
UR: [calling station's call sign]
R1: Blank
R2: Blank
MY: [listening station's call sign]

During the Contact (Calling Station)
UR: [listening station's call sign]
R1: Blank
R2: Blank
MY: [calling station's call sign]

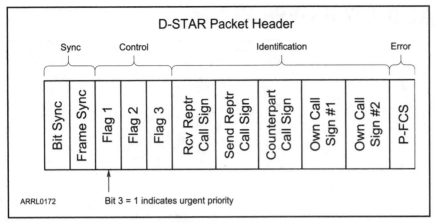

D-STAR Packet Header

| Sync | | Control | | | Identification | | | | | Error |

Bit Sync | Frame Sync | Flag 1 | Flag 2 | Flag 3 | Rcv Reptr Call Sign | Send Reptr Call Sign | Counterpart Call Sign | Own Call Sign #1 | Own Call Sign #2 | P-FCS

ARRL0172

Bit 3 = 1 indicates urgent priority

Figure 4-13— Bit 3 of the Flag byte 1 is used to indicate the emergency condition.

Although this seems like a lot of call sign programming, the presence of the call signs in D-STAR packets lets the radio acquire them automatically. D-STAR radios have special keys to set up the radio to call CQ, respond to a caller, or use a repeater.

Emergencies

D-STAR also provides an "all-call" function to alert all stations within range that an urgent or emergency situation exists. **Figure 4-13** shows the D-STAR header once again. There are three bytes that make up the control flags. Each bit of these three bytes has a separate meaning.

Bit 3 of the Flag byte 1 is used to indicate the emergency condition. Under normal conditions, bit 3 is *clear* (equal to 0). The bit can be *set* (equal to 1) to indicate that an emergency situation exists. Whenever a packet is received with this bit set to a 1 instead of a 0, the receiving radio ignores its current squelch settings and opens the speaker so that the received audio is heard.

The IC-91AD uses the "(decimal point)/EMR/DTMF" key to control the EMR function. If the key is pressed and held, a series of three short and one long beeps are heard, the "EMR" indicator is shown on the display, and all further packets will carry the emergency flag. To turn off the

EMR function, the key is pressed and held again.

Calling a Specific Station

There are two ways to call a specific station using a D-STAR radio. The first is to operate as if using analog FM. Set Counterpart Call Sign to "CQC-QCQ" and call the station by voice. For example, "N9JA, N9JA, are you on frequency? This is W7JRL." If N9JA is listening and does not have the special squelch functions DCS or CCS enabled, W7JRL's call will be heard.

The second is to make a call directed specifically to N9JA by setting Counterpart Call Sign to N9JA as shown in **Figure 4-14**. That way, if N9JA has set his radio to use the Call Sign Squelch (CSS), the receiver will detect N9JA in the packets and output your voice.

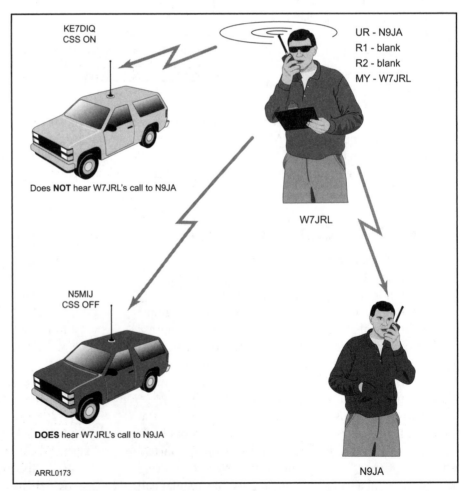

Figure 4-14—The alternative way to call a specific station is shown in this example where a call is directed specifically to N9JA by setting *Counterpart Call Sign* to N9JA

Using a Repeater

In the analog FM world, sub-audible CTCSS tones are often used to control access to a repeater. You must know the correct tone or the repeater receiver will not relay your voice to the transmitter. The D-STAR equivalent is the call sign stored in R1. If R1 is left blank or the call sign does not match the D-STAR repeater on the selected frequency, the repeater will not relay your signal.

The following sets of call signs assume that both users are using the same repeater — the most common type of repeater operation.

Calling CQ (Calling Station)
UR: CQCQCQ
R1: [Repeater's call sign]
R2: Blank
MY: [calling station's call sign]
Responding to a CQ and during the QSO (Responding Station)
UR: [calling station's call sign]
R1: [Repeater's call sign]
R2: Blank
MY: [listening station's call sign]
During the Contact (Calling Station)
UR: [listening station's call sign]
R1: [Repeater's call sign]
R2: Blank
MY: [calling station's call sign]

Making a Contact within a D-STAR Zone

In an analog system of linked repeaters, to make a call on the entire system the user might have to enter a special DTMF tone or sequence of tones to send the signal to all of the repeaters. In a D-STAR zone, the same function is performed by adding a slash character "/" before the repeater's call sign as follows:

Calling CQ (Calling Station)
UR: CQCQCQ
R1: /[Repeater's call sign] - note the slash in front of the call sign
R2: Blank
MY: [calling station's call sign]
Responding to a CQ and during the QSO (Responding Station)
UR: [calling station's call sign]
R1: [Responding station repeater's call sign] - note, no slash
R2: [Calling station repeater's call sign]
MY: [responding station's call sign]
During the Contact (Calling Station)
UR: [responding station's call sign]
R1: [Calling station repeater's call sign]
R2: [Responding station repeater's call sign]
MY: [calling station's call sign]

As before, the D-STAR radio will automatically acquire the necessary call signs from the packets, allowing the user to set up the radio in a few key presses.

D-STAR INTERNET GATEWAY DETAILS

The D-STAR gateway is not a "thing", but rather a "connection." The gateway is software that runs on a PC connected to the controller of a D-STAR repeater as shown in **Figure 4-15**. The PC has to be supplied with a broadband Internet connection, through which it can exchange data with any other gateway or D-STAR server worldwide.

Automatic and Manual Functions

Some functions of the gateway are automatic. For example, the call sign registry is accessed automatically to locate

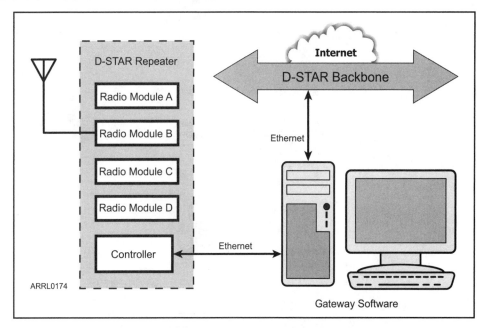

Figure 4-15— The gateway is software that runs on a PC connected to the controller of a D-STAR repeater.

KE4ROC (left) and KE4RNB proudly display their ICOM D-STAR repeater in Huntsville, Alabama.

The Directed Gateway

There are no "link control" signals required to connect and disconnect the repeaters. In a sense, all D-STAR repeaters are connected all the time and it is up to the users to decide when and where their signals should be heard! Unlike analog repeaters where linked systems share every signal they can hear, the D-STAR gateway only sends digitized signals to other repeaters when directed to do so by the information in a received D-STAR packet.

This also means that you can't "listen in" on a remote D-STAR repeater by switching on a link. The only time you will hear a signal from a remote D-STAR system is when the station that generates the signal directs the gateway to send it to your repeater or repeater zone.

the current repeater on which a specific call sign is registered. Another automatic function is the regular update of the database of the Internet Protocol (IP) addresses for other D-STAR gateways. That update occurs several times every day.

To the repeater user, though, most D-STAR functions that use the gateway require some kind of manual direction to be activated or initiated. For example, to call a friend using a different D-STAR repeater, you must direct your local D-STAR repeater to use its gateway to locate them. When making a CQ call outside the local D-STAR zone, you must direct your local repeater to the appropriate repeater system through the gateway.

Gateway Call Sign Conventions

The Receiver Repeater Call Sign field contains the necessary information to route signals through the D-STAR network by using a gateway. D-STAR packets not being relayed to other repeaters aren't handled by the gateway and so aren't heard elsewhere.

Adding a "G" to a repeater call in the Receiver Repeater Call Sign field tells the D-STAR repeater to send the transmission via the gateway. The "G" must be in the 8th available space in the call sign, so if the repeater has a 4-character call sign, three spaces must be added before the "G." **Figure 4-16** shows the necessary call sign set up to make a call on a remote repeater by using a gateway.

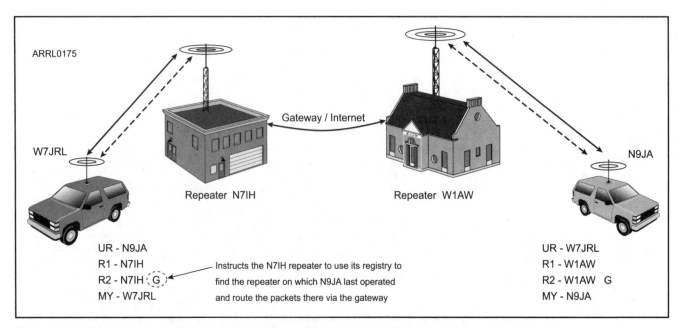

ARRL0175

Gateway / Internet

W7JRL

Repeater N7IH

Repeater W1AW

N9JA

UR - N9JA
R1 - N7IH
R2 - N7IH (G) ————— Instructs the N7IH repeater to use its registry to
MY - W7JRL   find the repeater on which N9JA last operated
                  and route the packets there via the gateway

UR - W7JRL
R1 - W1AW
R2 - W1AW G
MY - N9JA

Figure 4-16—The necessary call sign set up to make a call on a remote repeater by using a gateway.

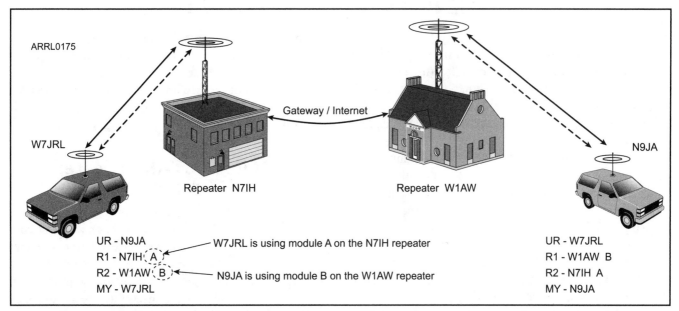

ARRL0175

Gateway / Internet

W7JRL

Repeater N7IH

Repeater W1AW

N9JA

UR - N9JA
R1 - N7IH A
R2 - W1AW B
MY - W7JRL

W7JRL is using module A on the N7IH repeater

N9JA is using module B on the W1AW repeater

UR - W7JRL
R1 - W1AW B
R2 - N7IH A
MY - N9JA

Figure 4-17—This example illustrates how two stations, W7JRL and N9JA, can have a contact even if they are operating on different repeaters on different bands.

In the figure, W7JRL is calling N9JA. W7JRL (My Call Sign, or MY) is sending D-STAR packets to the N7IH repeater. That requires W7JRL to have programmed Sender Repeater Call Sign (R1) with N7IH. Similarly, N9JA's R1 call sign is set to W1AW. N7IH and W1AW can be anywhere there is an Internet connection.

For W7JRL to call N9JA without knowing what repeater N9JA is using, W7JRL uses the automatic registry lookup of the N7IH gateway. This is accomplished by adding the "G" at the end of the R1 call sign. That tells the N7IH gateway software to look in its copy of the call sign registry (updated several times each day) for the repeater through which N9JA last made a transmission. When W7JRL calls N9JA, the N7IH repeater then knows to where to route the digitized audio signals. If N9JA is listening to the W1AW repeater, the call from W7JRL will be heard.

When W7JRL's call is heard, N9JA's radio should automatically save W7JRL's call along with W7JRL's repeater call sign — the Sender's Repeater Call Sign. This allows N9JA to reply immediately, without having to enter any call signs. The resulting set of call signs for W7JRL and N9JA to have a contact is shown in the figure.

What if W7JRL just wants to make a general call for a contact on the W1AW repeater? In that case, "CQCQCQ" is sent in the Your Call Sign (UR) field and the call is heard by everyone listening to the output of the W1AW repeater.

Cross-band Operation

D-STAR repeaters can support up to four radio modules as shown in Figure 4-15. The modules can be on any combination of bands. Currently, ICOM supplies modules for 144 and 440 MHz and 1.2 GHz. More than one module

can be on the same band, assuming that adequate filtering is available to prevent *desense*. Each module is assigned a unique letter identifier; A, B, C, or D.

Usually, your signal and those of the stations you contact will be on the same band. In this case, no module identification letter needs to be added to the Sender Repeater Call Sign field. The controller will cause your repeated signal to be transmitted on the same band on which it was received.

You may also choose to specify the output module explicitly and if the module chosen operates on a different band, you are then operating *cross-band*! This works similarly to an analog repeater system; the signal from one station is received and demodulated on one band and then routed to a transmitter whose output is on a different band. The other station's signal takes the opposite path.

In D-STAR systems, the modules (up to four) are selected by adding the module identification letter after the repeater call sign. The controller uses the letter to route the information between modules.

The D-STAR gateway allows cross-band operation across the D-STAR network just as if the modules were all in the same equipment cabinet. **Figure 4-17** illustrates how two stations, W7JRL and N9JA, can have a contact even if they are operating on different repeaters on different bands. As with single-band gateway operation, the D-STAR radios should acquire the necessary call sign information from the received packets to make replying automatic.

Just as with analog repeater systems, however, if you choose to specify the module the station you are calling must be listening on that band. Otherwise, they will not hear your call. Unlike analog systems, you can allow the D-STAR gateway to determine the proper module by using the call sign registry.

THE ICOM D-STAR REPEATER

Like most repeaters, the actual equipment consists of several specialized pieces of hardware. **Figure 4-18** shows a repeater that has four modules (the actual RF transceivers), a *controller*, an RF link, and a gateway PC with Internet link. This is a complete ICOM D-STAR repeater. (Antennas and other accessory equipment are not shown.)

At a minimum, a D-STAR repeater must have a controller and at least one module. The functionality of this isolated repeater would be quite limited because it would not have access to the D-STAR network for the call sign registry or any kind of zone communications with other D-STAR repeaters.

By adding the ICOM ID-RP2L RF link, the repeater can be linked to other D-STAR repeaters. If one of the linked repeaters has an Internet gateway, a D-STAR zone is formed. So this simple repeater — controller, module, and link--can provide all of the D-STAR network services.

Repeater Call Sign

You will need a unique call sign for the repeater, such as a club call sign. The same call sign can not be used in two different "roles" in the D-STAR network. (eg, the repeater call sign can not also be your individual call sign.) The call sign may not be used anywhere else in the D-STAR network. It is OK to reuse the call sign outside the D-STAR network, such as on HF or for an analog repeater.

ICOM D-STAR Repeater Components

One ID-RP2C repeater controller is required for each D-STAR repeater. Modules can not function without a controller. The controller is a microprocessor-baser computer system that supervises the modules, routes digital voice and data signals amongst them, and provides the interface to the gateway or RF link that connects the repeater to others in the D-STAR network.

D-STAR repeater modules perform the same functions as do transmitters and receivers in an analog repeater system. Modules do not include the duplexers necessary for the receiver and transmitter to share the antenna. A separate antenna connection is required for each module.

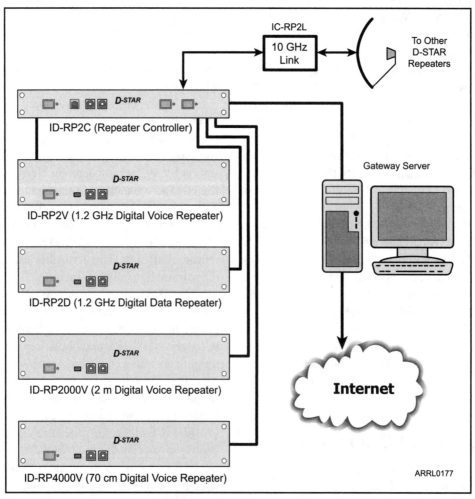

Figure 4-18—The repeater shown here has four modules: (the actual RF transceivers), a controller, an RF link, and a gateway PC with Internet link.

The modules process only D-STAR digital signals. An analog signal on a D-STAR module's input frequency is not demodulated or retransmitted.

The currently available ICOM D-STAR repeater modules are:

RP2D	1.2 GHz, 128k Digital Data (DD)
RP2V	1.2 GHz Digital Voice (DV)
RP4000V	440 MHz Digital Voice (DV)
RP2000V	144 MHz Digital Voice (DV)

Each module is connected to the controller at a separate *port*. There are four module ports on the controller and each can be connected to a DD or DV module. The recommended configuration for a full repeater system is:

Port 1	RP2D
Port 2	RP4000V
Port 3	RP2000V
Port 4	RP2V

Note that the interfaces between the controller and other ICOM modules or equipment are proprietary to ICOM equipment.

Configuring an ICOM D-STAR Repeater

To program the repeater controller and frequencies you will need:

- A *Windows*-based PC with at least 1 Ethernet and 1 USB port (1.1 or 2.0)
- USB A to B cable
- Ethernet cable (not a *crossover* cable)

Configuring a D-STAR Repeater Controller

Connect the Ethernet cable to the 10-BASE-T jack (an RJ-45 modular connector) on the controller's front panel. Configure the PC's Internet TCP/IP protocol to manually enter an IP address for the connection. (This is done via the *Windows Network Connections* window.)

Start the IC-RP2C configuration software and enter the controller's IP address in the "Network Setup" screen. The default IP addresses for the controller as shipped from ICOM are either 172.16.0.1 or 172.16.0.10. Click "OK". The ID-RP2C configuration software window will appear.

Click the "Read" button. In the subsequent "Network Password" window enter the password, which is "PASSWORD". You will now see the ID-RP2C configuration

software window as shown in **Figure 4-19**.

Step One — Enter the repeater's call sign. Remember that this must be a unique call sign within the entire D-STAR network. This is the repeater's D-STAR network identity to all D-STAR users.

Step Two — Select a "module configuration" from the drop down menu. The example shown is for a single DD module and three DV modules. Select the configuration that matches your repeater.

Step Three — Enable the active modules by clicking in the check box. If your repeater has fewer than four modules, the lower checkboxes and labels will be blank or grayed-out. The modules must be physically connected to

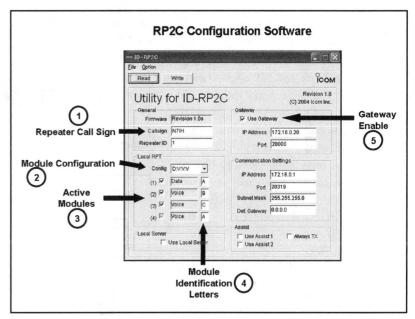

Figure 4-19—The ID-RP2C configuration software window.

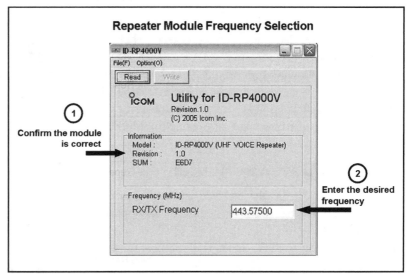

Figure 4-20—The frequency programming window is part of the repeater modules software.

Port 1 to 4 on the controller in exactly the same order as shown on this screen.

Step Four — Assign each active module a different identification letter. These are the letters by which users will identify the modules on which they want to operate. If ID-RP2V or ID-RP2D modules are included in the system, they must both be assigned the letter "A". This is due to the controller's internal software requirements.

Step Five — If the repeater will use an Internet gateway, click "Enable Gateway" to tell the controller that the gateway interface will be active.

Configuring an ICOM D-STAR Repeater Module

The D-STAR repeater module's control and programming is done using a USB interface on the module. There are two USB ports on each repeater module; one for the transmit (TX) frequency and the other for the receive (RX) frequency. Plug the USB A-B cable into the module and computer.

The *Windows* "Add New Hardware" wizard will be launched by your PC and the appropriate USB drivers will be installed. Launch the repeater modules software, which will then interrogate the module and display the frequency programming window shown in **Figure 4-20**. Enter the desired frequency for the module and click OK.

ICOM D-STAR GATEWAY CONFIGURATION AND OPERATION

The D-STAR Internet gateway must be assigned a fixed or *static IP address* and be provided with a broadband Internet connection, such as those provided by a DSL or cable connection. Whether your Internet connection router is a standalone device or included in a broadband gateway modem-router, it will need to provide or implement the following:

■ Class "A" internal *subnet* (LAN) 10.0.0.1 / 255.0.0.0
■ Port forwarding
■ Setting a fixed IP address, such as for *PPoE* for *WAN*

Note also that ICOM's gateway software is a proprietary, licensed vendor product, and can not be copied, shared or re-distributed. It is not part of the open D-STAR protocol.

If you are unfamiliar with the *Linux* operating system or with basic computer networking, it is strongly recommended that you obtain assistance before attempting to install or configure D-STAR gateway systems. For all of the following instructions and when editing or entering data, pay particularly close attention to detail. The syntax of the information is very important--errors will likely cause the software to fail or operate improperly.

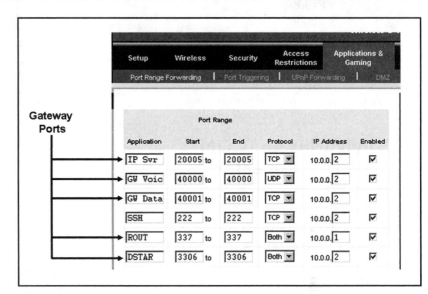

Figure 4-21—The port forwarding configuration screen for the Linksys WRV54G router.

Gateway Router

The gateway router--the interface between the gateway server and the Internet--must be configured to support the server software as follows:
■ Make sure the router's "local IP" settings are set as follows:
■ Local IP address: 10.0.0.1
■ Subnet mask: 255.0.0.0

Set the router to forward the following ports:
■ Data sync: 20005, Protocol - TCP, IP Address - 10.0.0.2
■ Voice RX: 40000, Protocol - UDP, IP Address - 10.0.0.2
■ Data RX: 40001, Protocol - TCP, IP Address - 10.0.0.2
■ SSH: 222, Protocol - TCP, IP Address - 10.0.0.2
■ Monitor: 3306, Protocol - TCP & UDP, IP Address - 10.0.0.2

Figure 4-21 shows the port forwarding configuration screen for the Linksys WRV54G router as an example. The router is then ready to support the gateway.

Gateway Server Configuration

The gateway software is hosted by a *Linux*-based PC.

All of the following instructions are based on the Fedora Core 3 or Fedora Core 4 version of *Linux*. The PC on which the gateway server and gateway software will run must meet the following minimum requirements:

- *Linux* OS (recommend Fedora Core 3 or 4)
- Pentium-grade 2.4 GHz or faster CPU
- At least 512MB RAM
- 2 LAN cards (NIC from Intel recommended)
- At least 10 GBytes hard drive free space

Ethernet Port Configuration

The host PC must have two Ethernet ports, eth0 and eth1. Eth0 is configured as a LAN port and will be connected to the router. Eth1 is configured to connect to the ID-RP2C controller. Both ports will have static IP addresses. In the "Ethernet Port" configuration screen set up Eth0 and Eth1 as follows:

Eth0
Select "Statically Set IP Address"
Address: 10.0.0.2
Subnet Mask: 255.0.0.0
Default Gateway Address: 10.0.0.1
Select "static IP" for eth1 as well and enter the proper settings.
Eth1
Select "Statically Set IP Address"
Address: 172.16.0.20
Subnet Mask: 255.0.0.0
Default Gateway Address: none

The gateway server must be physically located at the repeater. The segment of the LAN that connects the controller to the gateway (Eth1 - 172.16.0.20) is very sensitive to latency!

Network Configuration

In the "Network Configuration" configuration screen, the DNS server's address should be set to 127.0.0.1.

D-STAR Gateway Database

You will need to create the local database used to maintain connections with other repeaters and services on the D-STAR network. This requires the following steps:
- Add the information shown in the configuration guide to the **named.conf** file as shown in the gateway software manual.
- Create a folder named "dsipsvd" in the /var/named/ chroot/var directory.
- Create the local database, named **dstar.local.db** in the /var/named/chroot/var/named/ directory. The database file should contain the information shown in the configuration guide--syntax is critical. Errors in the

"named" service configuration are a common cause for the gateway to not operate properly.
- Re-start the Linux "named" service.
- From the Edit Runlevel menu, select Runlevel 3
- Click "named" and then Restart
- From the Edit Runlevel menu, select Runlevel 5
- Click "named" and then Restart

Use a terminal window to test the router and verify that the correct IP address has been entered by entering "dig router.dstar.local" In the "ANSWER SECTION" you should see the router's IP address - 10.0.0.1.

Trust Servers

A trust server, USRoot, is provided as a service to the D-STAR community by K5TIT in Dallas, TX. You can use your own private trust server to create your own D-STAR network or you can link to the USRoot trust server in Dallas, if desired. Any PC running the D-STAR gateway software can be configured to be a trust server to create your own private network.

Gateway Software

The D-STAR gateway software is supplied as a self-extracting file. Be sure to extract the program to the "dstar" folder in the "root" directory.

Once the software has been installed, open the file **dsipsvd.conf** to set up the following pieces of information:
- TRUST_SERVER - the IP address of the trust server you have chosen
- ZR_CALLSIGN - the call sign of the zone repeater (the repeater with the D-STAR gateway for your zone)
- IPSV_ADDR - the IP address of the gateway server
- DNS_ZONE_FILE_PATH - the location of the **dstar. local.db** file
- NAMED_PID_FILE - the location of the **named.pid** file

Next, acquire the MAC address of the Eth0 port by typing the command "arp" in a terminal window. Look for the line that shows Eth0 connected to an IP address of 10.0.0.1. Record the MAC address on that line. That is the MAC address of the NIC card of the Eth0 port.

Open the **dsgwd.conf** file and set up the following pieces of information:
- ZR_ADDR - the address of the zone repeater server, set to 172.16.0.10
- ZR_CALLSIGN - the call sign of the zone repeater
- DNS_MAC - the MAC address of the Ethernet device used to connect to the DNS server.

In the **blank** file, add the following lines to set up the D-STAR log files (the first line, beginning with #, is a comment):

for D-STAR
local0.*   /var/log/dsgwd.log
local2.*   /var/log/dsipsvd.log

Make sure to type "local" immediately before the number with no spaces.

Next, modify the startup script **/etc/rc.d/rc.local** to automatically run the D-STAR gateway software by adding this line anywhere in the file:

/dstar/exec-mgsv

Set the software's default runlevel to "3" by opening the file **/etc/inittab** and changing the line

id:#:initdefault:

so that the pound sign (#) is replaced by "3".

This completes the configuration of the D-STAR gateway software. Restart the Linux system.

Testing the Gateway

After the system starts, from the SSH Shell, type:

ps –ef | grep dstar

and you should see at least the following pair of programs running:

/dstar/dsipsvddsipsvd - this is the gateway server
/dstar/dsgwd/dsgwd - this is the gateway itself

Without both programs running, the gateway will not be functional! If the programs are not running, check the log file at:

/var/log

The log files from both programs should be being saved as:

dsipsvd.log
dsgwd.log

Once your gateway is up and running, it will synchronize itself with the rest of the D-STAR network. The easiest way to see if it synchronized is to look at the **dstar.local.db** file.

Open the file:

/var/named/chroot/var/named/dstar.local.db

If the gateway has been synchronized, you will see a list of other D-STAR gateway servers and their IP addresses as shown in **Figure 4-22**.

The gateway software uses 3 tables:

RIP – Reserved IP addresses
GIP – Gateway IP addresses
MNG – Call sign manage table

The backup tables are stored in the **/var/dsipsvd** folder. The files being used by the gateway are resident in memory after being downloaded from the trust server. You can "write" the tables to a text file to view, if desired. You can not edit them directly. All files are updated / merged automatically with the trust server and all the other gateways on the network at least once a day.

Adding Users to the D-STAR Network

Any user can operate locally on a D-STAR repeater, with or without their call sign in the registry. Only users that have been added to the gateway registry are allowed to cross the D-STAR gateway and access the global D-STAR network. Once a user is added to the D-STAR gateway, they have gateway rights via any D-STAR gateway that is configured to use the same trust server.

Each user call sign is assigned a fixed IP address. The available IP addresses are assigned in blocks of 32 and can be viewed by entering the command

cat /tmp/dsipsvd-cmdout

Record the range of IP addresses for use in registering new calls.

The exact syntax of the "add user" command is shown in the gateway software manual. Along with the range of IP addresses, the following information is required:

■ User ID — the users call sign, it must be 8 characters long, add spaces to pad

■ Area Repeater Call Sign — the system call sign with the letter [A] in the 8th position, use spaces between the call sign and the [A]

■ Zone Repeater Call Sign — the zone repeater call sign, it must be 8 characters long, add spaces to pad

■ GW IP Address — the public fixed IP address of the gateway server

■ Users Assigned IP Address — the address assigned to the user by the local address coordinator (one of the IP addresses recorded earlier)

■ Alias Name for DNS — the user's call

Figure 4-22— If the gateway has been synchronized, you will see a list of other D-STAR gateway servers and their IP addresses.

sign, in lower case, padded with spaces at the end if necessary.

The following is an example of a "add user" command to add W7JRL to the N7IH registry. * represents a space in this example:

add W7JRL71*|N7IH9**A|N7IH9***|65.102.167.146|1 0.140.194.xxx|w7jrl71" > /tmp/dsipsvd-cmdin

Going Live!

Before attempting to go "live" on the D-STAR network you must verify that you are 100% functional on the ICOM test system. If you have any questions, contact ICOM. This will avoid corrupting the network databases that would inconvenience many D-STAR users.

Once operational on the "test" network, you need to "kill & clean" your gateway, change the TRUST_SERVER IP address, and re-boot the gateway PC. Simply restarting the gateway software will not do the job!

To "clean" your system and start fresh (on the live network), begin by killing all active D-STAR services:

■ Execute a 'ps -ef | grep dstar' command. This will provide the process numbers for the dsgwd & dsipsvd processes.

■ Execute a 'kill xxx' command, where 'xxx' is the process number revealed in step one, for each of the two processes.

■ Execute a 'rm /var/dsipsvd/*.*' command. This should completely clear the /var/dsipsvd directory.

■ Edit the file /var/named/chroot/var/named/dstar.local. db with a text editor and delete any call sign entries after "#DSTAR A RECORD".E

■ Execute a 'cat /etc/dsipsvd.conf' command, and ensure that your TRUST_SERVER points to the proper server IP for the desired network. Use a text editor to change the TRUST_SERVER IP, if needed.

If you are creating or cleaning your own D-STAR network, you can execute the cleanup on the TRUST_SERVER, and have it ready. (Do not perform this step if you are joining an existing D-STAR network.)

■ Execute a 'reboot' command on your gateway.

The gateway will run and download new database files from the TRUST_SERVER, then re-sync with each of the other gateways.

All gateways pointed to the same trust server share the same GIP, RIP and MNG tables. These tables can not be changed or "cleaned-up" independently. Going live requires that all connected gateways to be "killed" and "cleaned" first.

Once all connected gateways are "killed", the trust server files can be edited, but only before any gateway is re-booted. When the gateways are "cleaned" and re-booted, they will download the new GIP, RIP and MNG tables from the TRUST_SERVER.

DIGITAL METEOR SCATTER AND MOONBOUNCE WITH WSJT

Although it sounds like science fiction, hams routinely use meteors and the Moon as radio reflectors. They've been doing it for decades. In the ham world, these activities are known as *meteor scatter* and *moonbounce* (or *EME*—Earth-Moon-Earth) respectively. Both rely on the principle that radio commu-

The Moon isn't just a pretty face. It's also a handy radio reflector.

Meteors are plunging into the Earth's atmosphere constantly-- even as you read this book.

nication can span great distances when signals are reflected from high-altitude objects.

Take meteors as an example. These space rocks plunge into Earth's atmosphere constantly. As you read these words, there are meteors streaking across the sky a few hundred miles above your head. It is estimated that the Earth sweeps up more than 100,000 tons of meteor debris each year. Most are the size of sand grains and even smaller. Of course, there are also much larger meteors that create spectacular displays in the night sky, particularly during events such as *meteor showers*.

A meteor is screaming along at tens of thousands of miles per hour when it enters our atmosphere. At such speeds the air molecules cannot easily slide by. Instead, they accumulate immediately in front of the meteor and are compressed under fantastic pressure. If you've ever studied how a diesel engine works, you know that when air in the engine cylinder is placed under high pressure by the piston, it heats up very quickly. The same thing happens to the air in front of the meteor. The molecules can't get out of the way fast enough and become squeezed until they create superheated plasma. It is this white-hot plasma that burns

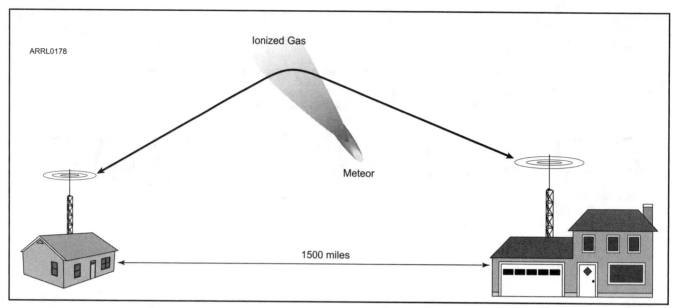

Figure 5-1— By bouncing signals off their ionized trails, hams can use meteors to communicate over distances of hundreds of miles, and potentially as far as 1500 miles.

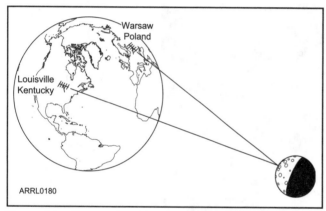

Figure 5-2— By using the Moon as a reflector, it is possible to communicate over thousands of miles here on Earth. The Moon need only be above your horizon and the horizon of the station you wish to contact at the same time.

and destroys the meteor, not simple friction. This plasma also creates a stream of ionized gas that trails behind the meteor. The ionization may only last a few seconds, but while it exists it acts as a mirror for radio waves. By bouncing signals off their ionized trails, hams can use meteors to communicate over distances of hundreds of miles, and potentially as far as 1500 miles. See **Figure 5-1**.

The Moon is a somewhat different matter. Having been our nighttime companion for a few billion years, the Moon,

unlike evanescent meteor trails, is constant and highly reliable. Its surface also reflects radio waves, although not as efficiently as ionized gas. Using the Moon as a radio reflector, hams thousands of miles apart can communicate. The rule is simple: the Moon must be simultaneiously above your horizon and the horizon of the station you want to talk to. See **Figure 5-2**.

The only problem with communicating by way of the Moon is distance and the resulting *path loss*. A round-trip to the Moon is a journey of nearly 500,000 miles. Any signal you send to another ham via the Moon is going to lose a *lot* of its energy along the way thanks to the *inverse square rule*: The decrease in strength of a radio signal is inversely proportional to the square of the change in distance from the antenna. Worse still, the signal returning from the Moon is again attenuated by the inverse square rule, thereby producing an overall inverse fourth-power effect. To compensate for the huge loss, you need serious RF (1000 W or more), high-gain antennas and sensitive receive systems.

The old-school approach to meteor scatter and moonbounce was to invest in large antennas and high-power RF amplifiers. CW was the mode of choice since a concentrated, narrow-bandwidth signal had the best chance to survive the journey and still be intelligible at the receiving station (this was especially true for moonbounce).

Then along came Joe Taylor, K1JT, and everything changed.

THE DEBUT OF *WSJT*

Joe Taylor, K1JT, has been a ham and a scientist throughout most of his life, but he attracted the media spotlight in 1993 when he won a Nobel Prize in Physics for the discovery of a new type of pulsar, a discovery that created new possibilities for the study of gravitation.

Joe was keenly aware of the many interesting things that were happening in the field of personal computer technology in the 1990s. In particular, the computer sound card was rapidly evolving from a simple entertainment device to a sophisticated digital signal processor. Like other pioneering radio amateurs, Joe was attracted to the idea that an inexpensive sound card could become a sensitive two-way analog/digital converter. A sound card can convert analog signals from a radio to digital data for processing within a computer. The same sound card can be instructed to create analog audio signals with various modulation schemes for transmission. With the increasing power of personal computers, it became apparent that a sound-card-equipped PC could function as a stand-alone digital communicator. All you needed was a radio.

In 1999, Peter Martinez, G3PLX, used this approach to create a new Amateur Radio digital communication mode known as *PSK31*. His *Windows*-based program used the computer sound card to digitize received signals. Once the analog signal had been converted to data, Peter's software applied digital signal processing (DSP) techniques to decode an encoded pattern of phase changes, thereby extracting text information for display on a computer monitor. Thanks to the power of DSP, even weak signals could be decoded with ease. When it was time to transmit, Peter's software accepted text from the keyboard and instructed the sound card to create a narrow, phase-shift-encoded output signal for the radio. With so many hams owning sound-card-equipped PCs, PSK31 caught on quickly and became the most popular HF digital communications mode used by amateurs today.

Joe Taylor also set out to devise a means to put the sound card to work in a practical ham application, but as a radio astronomer his focus was on the heavens. He was aware that some hams were already using high-speed Morse code communication as a means to exploit short-duration meteor burns. They sent brief messages at 200 words per minute or faster. The receiving stations then had to slow the pulse streams to more reasonable speeds for manual decoding. This was a tedious process, however, and it was limited to amateurs who had the ability to decipher Morse code accurately.

Joe believed that a more efficient alternative would be to develop a method of digital *text* communication that could also work with very short meteor burns. If such an application existed, hams could operate meteor scatter any time of the day or night without having to master Morse code. As a bonus, the system could use a modulation scheme more efficient than standard Morse code.

A similar approach could also apply DSP techniques to squeeze information from extremely weak signals—the kind that travel to the Moon and back. With the right software, it would be possible to do digital moonbounce with less elaborate antennas and much less output power (on the order of a couple of hundred watts).

In 2001 Joe Taylor finally unveiled his software masterpiece—a suite of applications known simply as *WSJT*.

The *WSJT* Suite

WSJT is available for both *Windows* and *Linux*. It is a software suite that supports five different operating modes:

- **FSK441** for meteor scatter
- **JT65** for moonbounce
- **JT6M**, optimized for meteor scatter on 6 meters
- **EME Echo** for measuring the echoes of your own signal from the Moon
- **CW** for moonbounce communication using 15 WPM Morse code

The software is available for free downloading from Joe Taylor's Web page at **physics.princeton.edu/pulsar/K1JT/**.

WSJT Technical Description

FSK441 uses four-tone frequency shift keying (FSK) at 41 baud. The frequencies of the audio tones are 882, 1323, 1764, and 2205 Hz. The FSK441 alphabet consists of 43 characters and each encoded character uses three tone intervals and therefore requires 3/441 seconds (approximately 2.3 ms) for transmission.

The four possible single-tone character codes, namely 000, 111, 222, and 333, are reserved for special use as shorthand messages. When sent repeatedly, these reserved characters generate pure single-frequency carriers. The shorthand messages are defined to mean "R26", "R27", "RRR", and "73", respectively. These messages are frequently used in meteor scatter QSOs after call signs have been exchanged.

JT6M uses 44-tone FSK with a synchronizing tone and 43 possible data tones, one for each character in the same set used for FSK441. The sync tone is at $1102500/1024 = 1076.66$ Hz and the 43 other possible tones are spaced at intervals of $11025/512 = 21.53$ Hz up to 2002.59 Hz. Transmitted symbols are keyed at a rate of 21.53 baud, so each one lasts for $1/21.53 = 0.04644$ seconds. Every third symbol is the sync tone, and each sync symbol is followed by two data symbols. The transmission rate of user data is therefore $(2/3) \times 21.53 = 14.4$ characters per second.

JT65 60-second transmit/receive sequences and carefully structured messages. Standard messages are compressed so that two call signs and a grid locator can be transmitted with just 71 bits. A 72nd bit serves as a flag to indicate that the message consists of arbitrary text (up to 13 characters) instead of call signs and a grid locator. Special formats allow other information such as call sign prefixes or numerical signal reports (in dB) to be substituted for the grid locator. The aim of source encoding is to compress the common messages used for EME QSOs into a minimum fixed number of bits. After compression, a Reed Solomon (63,12) error-correcting code converts 72-bit user messages into sequences of 63 six-bit channel symbols.

Unlike the meteor scatter *WSJT* modes, JT65 requires tight synchronization of time and frequency between the transmitter and receiver. Each transmission is divided into 126 contiguous time intervals or symbols, each of length $4096/11025 = 0.372$ s. Within each interval the waveform is a constant-amplitude sinusoid at one of 65 pre-defined frequencies. Frequency changes between intervals are accomplished in a phase-continuous manner. Half of the channel symbols are devoted to a pseudo-random synchronizing vector interleaved with the encoded information symbols. The sync vector allows calibration of relative time

and frequency offsets between transmitter and receiver.

A transmission nominally begins at $t = 1$ s after the start of a UTC minute and finishes at $t = 47.8$ s. The synchronizing tone is at $11025 \times 472/4096 = 1270.5$ Hz, and is normally sent in each interval having a "1" in the following pseudo-random sequence:

1001100011111101010001011001000111001111011011 11000110101011001

1010101001000000110000000110100101101010110 001001000011111111

Encoded user information is transmitted during the 63 intervals not used for the sync tone. Each channel symbol generates a tone at frequency $1275.8 + 2.6917 \, Nm$ Hz, where N is the value of the six-bit symbol, $0 \le N \le 63$, and m is 1, 2, or 4 for JT65 sub-modes A, B, or C. The signal report "OOO" is conveyed by reversing sync and data positions in the transmitted sequence. Shorthand messages dispense with the sync vector and use intervals of 1.486 s (16,384 samples) for the alternating tones. The lower frequency is always 1270.5 Hz, the same as that of the sync tone, and the frequency separation is $26.92 \, nm$ Hz with $n = 2, 3, 4$ for the messages RO, RRR, and 73.

YOUR *WSJT* STATION

The type of station you create for *WSJT* depends on the activities you wish to pursue. The one common element is the computer: a 1 GHz or faster PC running either *Windows* or *Linux*. You will also need a sound card (or pre-installed motherboard sound chipset).

To connect the computer and sound card to your transceiver, you will need a *sound card interface*. See **Figure 5-3**. This device allows your computer to switch your radio automatically between transmit and receive. Many interfaces also provide audio isolation for cleaner transmit and receive signals. You don't need an elaborate interface; just a simple model will do nicely. Check the advertising

pages of *QST* magazine and you'll find interfaces from manufacturers such as West Mountain Radio (**www.westmountainradio.com**), MFJ (**www.mfjenterprises.com**), TigerTronics (**www.tigertronics.com**) and others.

As you approach the RF portion of your *WSJT* station, you have several options to consider.

■**Meteor Scatter on 6 Meters**: This is the simplest station configuration. All you need is an SSB transceiver with 6 meter coverage and a basic antenna system. You will work more stations with a directional antenna such as a Yagi or Moxon design, but this isn't strictly necessary. Six meters is the easiest band for meteor scatter

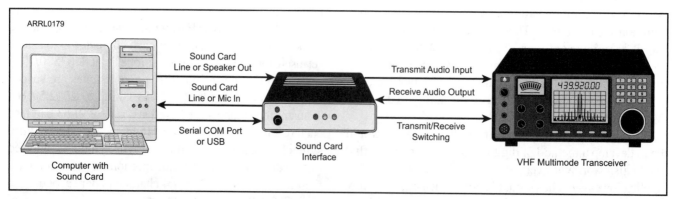

Figure 5-3—The sound card interface acts as the bridge between your radio and your computer. Its primary job is to handle transmit/receive switching. Some sound card interfaces also provide audio signal isolation and other features.

René Hasper, PE1L (left) and Peter de Graaf, PJ4/PA3CNX, set up this portable 2-meter moonbounce station on the Caribbean island of Bonaire and made more than 200 digital contacts using WSJT. They used four 2-meter Yagi antennas in a phased array. According to Peter, they contacted several stations who were using only single Yagi antennas and about 500 W output.

need directional antennas. The antennas will also need to be elevated on towers or roof tops to clear trees and other obstacles that attenuate the 2-meter signal. An SSB transceiver with 2-meter coverage at 100 W output should suffice, although some hams prefer to add amplifiers to boost the RF output to several hundred watts.

■ **Moonbounce**: Even with the advantage of *WSJT*, your odds of success at moonbounce are directly related to your hardware investment. Yes, it is possible to complete *WSJT* moonbounce contacts with 100 W on 2 meters and a single long Yagi antenna. However, conditions have to be just right and the station at the other end of the path must be running high power with high-gain antennas. In other words, *he* has to do most of the work to make the contact!

To enjoy *WSJT* moonbounce contacts on a *consistent* basis, a better bet is an SSB transceiver feeding an RF power amplifier (500 W output or more) and an antenna system consisting of two or more Yagis connected in phase. The antennas should be turned with an azimuth/elevation rotator that will allow them to move up and down as well as side to side. This will permit the antenna system to track the Moon as it moves across the sky. The station will also need a receive preamplifier mounted at the antenna to give the weak signals a boost before they enter the feed line. Look for an RF switched preamp. This device incorporates an RF-sensitive relay that protects the preamplifier circuits by automatically switching them out of the line whenever you transmit. For more detailed information about assembling a moonbounce station, see the *ARRL Handbook*.

and many hams have enjoyed success with simple wire antennas and even ground-mounted verticals. In terms of RF output, 100 W is adequate.

■ **Meteor Scatter on 2 Meters**: Two meters is more popular than 6 meters for meteor scatter, but it is also more challenging. To ensure success on this band you'll definitely

WSJT SOFTWARE SETUP

Once you've downloaded and installed *WSJT*, you'll need to perform the initial configuration.

Select **Options** from the **Setup** menu and enter your call sign and grid locator. If you don't know your grid locator, or how to find it, get on the Web and go to **www.arrl.org/locate/gridinfo.html**. You'll find complete instructions there.

In the box labeled **PTT Port** enter the number of the serial port you will use for T/R control (for example

1 if you will use COM1). This is the port you're using for your sound card interface. Enter 0 if you will use VOX control (not recommended if you are running high power). If you are running *WSJT* under *Linux*, enter the actual device name, for example /dev/ttyS0.

Close the **Options** window and tap the **F7** key to choose the **FSK441A** mode. Select **Open** from the **File** menu. Navigate to the RxWav\Samples folder in your *WSJT* home directory on your hard drive and open the

WSJT setup screen.

file recorded from W8WN. Click **DECODE** to process it. When this file has been decoded, click with the right mouse button around the location of the signal (known as a *ping*) at t = 18 s on the graphical display, and observe the decoded text that appears. If you click on the static crashes around t = 1 s or elsewhere on the green line, you will see garbage text. Click **ERASE** to clear the text and graphical areas. You can click **DECODE** to decode the full file again.

Take note of two numbers in the first panel of the status bar at lower left of the main screen. After *WSJT* has been running for a minute or so they should stabilize at values close to 1.0000. If both numbers are between 0.9995 and 1.0005, the input and output sampling rates of your soundcard are close to the nominal 11025 Hz. If either number is outside this range, enter it as **Rate in** (first number) or **Rate out** (second number) on the **Options** screen. *WSJT* will then make necessary adjustments for

the incorrect hardware sampling rate or rates.

You will need a method of setting your computer clock to an accuracy of one second or better, and keeping it set. Many operators use an Internet-based clock-setting program, while others use a broadcast service such as GPS or WWVB. If you are using *Windows XP* or *Vista*, the clock setting application is built in. You'll find in under **DATE and TIME** in the **CONTROL PANEL**.

Adjusting Signal Levels

If your computer has more than one sound card, select the desired device numbers for **Audio In** and **Audio Out**. The **Console Window** offers a menu of choices.

Once you've selected your sound device, turn on your radio and tune it to a clear frequency so that only background noise is sent to the sound card. On 6 meters, for example, try 50.260 MHz. That's the calling frequency for *WSJT* meteor scatter activity on that band.

Click **MONITOR** to start audio sampling and select **Options | Rx volume control** on the SpecJT screen to bring up the sound card input mixer.

Adjust a slider on the audio mixer and/or your receiver gain control(s) to bring the signal level close to what *WSJT* considers "0 dB" as indicated on the bar graph at lower right of the SpecJT screen. The signal level is also displayed on the status bar at bottom of the main *WSJT* window.

Now press **F7** to enter FSK441A mode. Select **Options | Tx volume control** to bring up the sound card output mixer. Click the **Tx1** button to be sure that T/R switching works and that audio tones are being sent from the computer to your radio. If everything is working as it should, your sound card interface should switch your transceiver into the transmit mode.

Adjust the slider on the audio output mixer to get the proper audio signal level for your transmitter. Watch your transceiver ALC meter. If you see any ALC activity, reduce the audio output level until it stops. Overdriving your radio will result in a distorted signal.

Digital Meteor Scatter and Moonbounce Frequencies

Frequency (MHz	Activity
50.185–50.195	JT65 Moonbounce
50.255—50.285	FSK441 and JT6M Meteor Scatter
50.260	FSK441 and JT6M Meteor Scatter Calling Frequency
144.115—144.135	JT65 Moonbounce
144.140	FSK441 Meteor Scatter Calling Frequency
222.085	FSK441 Meteor Scatter
432.060–432.070	JT65 Moonbounce
1296.060–1296.070	JT65 Moonbounce

For more information see the WSJTGroup page on the Web at **www.ykc.com/wa5ufh/**.

ON THE AIR WITH *WSJT*

Digital meteor scatter and moonbounce contacts are usually just that—contacts, not true conversations. Given the weak signals and tenuous conditions, the idea is to simply send enough information to constitute a valid contact:

- An exchange of call signs
- An exchange of signal reports
- An exchange of acknowledgements

WSJT is designed to facilitate making such minimal QSOs under difficult conditions, and the process can be made easier if you follow standard operating practices. The recommended procedure is as follows:

1. If you have received less than both calls from the other station, send both calls.

2. If you have received both calls, send both calls and a signal report.

3. If you have received both calls and a report, send R plus your signal report.

4. If you have received R plus signal report, send RRR.

5. If you have received RRR — that is, a definite acknowledgment of all of your information — the QSO is "officially" complete. However, the other station may not know this, so it is conventional to send 73s (or some other conversational information) to signify that you are done.

Slightly different procedures may be used in different parts of the world, or in the different operating modes. Typing the **F5** key will cause *WSJT* to pop up a screen that reminds you of the recommended procedures.

To prepare for making a QSO, enter the other station's call sign in the **To radio** box and click **LOOKUP** and **GENSTDMSGS** to generate a sequence of the commonly used messages. If **Lookup** does not find the call sign in the database file CALL3.TXT, you may enter the grid locator manually. Decide whether you or the other station will transmit first, and check or uncheck **Tx First** appropriately. Select the message for your next transmission by clicking in the small circle to the right of the message text. Click **AUTO** to start an automatic sequence of transmission and reception intervals. You can switch messages while a transmission is in progress by clicking on one of the **Tx** buttons to the right of the circles.

Real-time spectral information is displayed graphically on the SpecJT screen. Spectrograms scroll horizontally in FSK441 and JT6M, and vertically in JT65. You can select one of several scrolling speeds at the top right of the SpecJT window.

At the end of each receiving period, *WSJT* displays various properties of a received signal on the main screen. A green line in the main graphical area illustrates signal strength vs. time, and other lines or images

display spectral information and synchronization results, depending on the mode.

Decoded text appears in the large box below the graphical area and is also written to a cumulative output file, ALL.TXT. The program's best estimate of **DF**, a detected signal's frequency offset, is included on each text line. The accuracy of these estimates is about ±25 Hz for FSK441 signals, ±10 Hz for JT6M, and ±3 Hz for JT65. Within these tolerances (and subject to the stability of oscillators and the propagation path) you should see consistent numbers in the DF column during any QSO that produces usable signals.

Double-clicking on a call sign in either one of the decoded text windows will cause that call sign to be copied into the **To radio** box. The corresponding grid locator will be looked up in the database and the call sign inserted appropriately into the message boxes **Tx1** and **Tx2**. If the decoded text line includes "CQ" before the selected call sign, message **Tx1** will be selected for your next transmission. Otherwise, **Tx2** will be selected. The status of **Tx First** may be changed if the time-stamp on the decoded message indicates this should be done and if **"Double-click on call sign sets TxFirst"** has been checked on the **Setup** menu.

Meteor Scatter with FSK441 and JT6M

The FSK441 and JT6M operating modes use 30-second for transmission and reception. When a reception interval has finished, the program looks for signal enhancements produced by short-lived reflections from

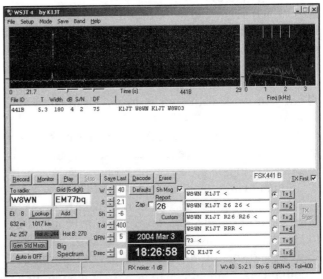

A meteor scatter signal is detected and decoded in the *WSJT* FSK441 mode.

meteor trails. You can often hear such pings when they occur, and you will see them as spikes on the green line and brighter colors in the waterfall spectrum. One or more lines of decoded text may result from each ping. By clicking in the graphical area you can force a decoding attempt at a particular spot in a record. You can also make the program decode in real time, just after hearing a ping, by clicking on the ping in the SpecJT display.

WSJT attempts to compensate for relative mistuning between transmitting and receiving stations. By default the frequency search range is ±400 Hz in FSK441 and JT6M modes. You can reduce the range by setting the value of **Tol** (for "tolerance") to a smaller value. Adjustments to the decoding parameters can be made at any time by right- or left-clicking on the parameter labels. **S** sets the minimum strength (in dB) for acceptable pings. **Clip** sets a parameter that establishes the program's immunity to broadband noise pulses. Set **Clip** to a value greater than 0 if static crashes are producing too many garbage decodes. All parameters can be reset to their default values for the mode in use by clicking the **Defaults** button.

In the FSK441 and JT6M modes, if DF lies outside the range ±100 Hz it will help to retune your receiver to compensate. Do this with your transceiver's RIT control, or by using split Rx/Tx VFOs. In JT6M mode you can accomplish the same thing by checking **Freeze** and using the keyboard right/left arrows to move **Freeze DF** (as displayed in the bottom-of-screen status bar) to the desired value. In general you should not change your transmitting frequency during a QSO, since your partner will be trying to tune you in at the same time.

In addition to the green line for overall signal strength, JT6M produces a yellow line showing the detected strength of a JT6M synchronizing tone. JT6M attempts to decode both individual pings and an "average message" based on the entire transmission, or selected portions thereof. An average message is flagged with an asterisk at the right end of the decoded text line. Clicking with the left mouse button decodes a 4 s block of data near the mouse pointer, while the right button decodes a 10 s segment. As in FSK441, with marginal signals you should experiment as necessary for best decoding. JT6M can work with signals many dB weaker than those required for FSK441. You will sometimes find that clicking on a smooth green line, even where nothing was heard and nothing can be seen, causes call signs or other information to pop up out of the noise.

Standard messages in FSK441 and JT6M are generated with the aid of templates defined on the **Setup | Options** screen. Default templates are provided conforming to standard operating practices in North America and Europe, and you can edit the templates to suit your own requirements. Your edits will be saved on program termination and restored when you restart *WSJT*. Normal

FSK441 and JT6M messages can contain any arbitrary text up to 28 characters. The supported character set is 0 1 2 3 4 5 6 7 8 9 A B C D E F G H I J K L M N O P Q R S T U V W X Y Z . , / # ? $ plus the space character.

FSK441 also provides a special shorthand format to transmit a few simple messages in a highly efficient way. Check **Sh Msg** to enable shorthand messages. The supported shorthands are R26, R27, RRR, and 73, and FSK441 sends pure tones at 882, 1323, 1764, or 2205 Hz to convey these messages. If activity levels are high enough that there could be some doubt about who has transmitted a shorthand message, it is better to use normal messages tagged with call signs or portions thereof.

A typical minimal QSO in FSK441 or JT6M modes might look something like the following:

1. CQ K1JT

2. K1JT W8WN

3. W8WN K1JT 27

4. JT R26

5. WN RRR

6. 73 W8WN

Don't move to the next message in your sequence until you have received your QSO partner's information from his sequence.

Moonbounce with JT65

JT65 has three sub-modes known as JT65A, B, and C. They are identical except for the spacing between transmitted tone intervals. At the present time JT65A is generally used on 50 MHz, JT65B on 144 and 432 MHz, and JT65C on 1.2 and 2.3 GHz. The B and C modes are slightly less sensitive than mode A, but progressively more tolerant of frequency drifts and rapid fading.

JT65 uses 60-second transmit/receive intervals. An incoming signal is analyzed only when the receiving sequence is complete. The resulting graphical display includes red and blue lines along with the green line. The additional curves summarize the program's attempts to synchronize with the received signal in frequency (red) and time (blue), both of which are necessary steps in decoding the message. You can set the minimum synchronizing threshold with the **Sync** parameter (default value = 1). Proper synchronization is indicated by a sharp upward spike in the red curve and a broader peak on the blue curve. Locations of the peaks correspond to the time and frequency offsets, DT and DF, between transmitter and receiver. EME signals have propagation delays of about 2.5 s and can have significant Doppler shifts. Along with clock and frequency errors, these effects

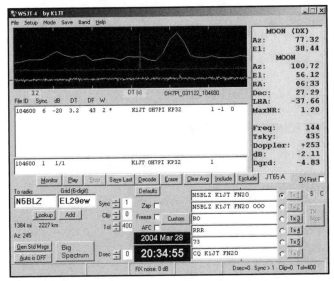

Moonbounce with WSJT.

contribute to the measured values of DT and DF.

JT65 is tolerant of frequency offsets up to ±600 Hz. Unless the "red spike" is close to the left or right edge of the plot area (see picture on page 14), retuning with RIT is optional. However, on bands above 432 MHz, where EME Doppler shifts can amount to several kHz or more, you may need to use RIT or split VFOs in order to acquire the desired signal. Once the program has synchronized on a JT65 signal, it's best to click on the red spike or on the sync tone in the SpecJT waterfall, check **Freeze**, and reduce **Tol** to 100 Hz or less. Then, in subsequent decoding attempts, *WSJT* will search a range of frequencies only ±**Tol** Hz around the selected **Freeze DF**.

In JT65 mode, double-clicking on the SpecJT waterfall or on the red curve in the main window sets **Freeze DF** to the selected frequency, turns **Freeze** on, sets **Tol** to 50 Hz, and invokes the decoder. Using this handy feature, you can quickly decode a transmission at several different values of DF. Colored vertical tick marks on the SpecJT frequency scale indicate the current setting of **Freeze DF** and the corresponding upper edge of the JT65 bandwidth (green ticks), and the frequencies of the shorthand message tones (red ticks). A horizontal green bar indicates the search range specified by **Tol** and centered on **Freeze DF**.

The JT65 decoder uses a multi-layered procedure. A full description of how it works is available at **http://pulsar.princeton.edu/~joe/K1JT/JT65.pdf**. If the soft-decision Reed Solomon decoder fails, a deeper search is made using a matched-filter approach. The decoder constructs a list of hypothetical messages by pairing each entry in the call sign database with "CQ" and with the home call sign of the user. Each trial message is encoded

as it would be done at the transmitter, including all of the forward error-control (FEC) symbols. The resulting patterns are then tested for good match with the received wave file. Even a single-character mismatch will prevent a decoding from being achieved. You can define the list of likely call signs in any way you choose. A default call sign database named CALL3.TXT is provided with *WSJT*, containing the calls of over 4800 stations known to have been active in weak-signal work on the VHF/UHF bands. It is strongly advised that you keep your list up to date and adapt it to your own requirements.

In addition to DT and DF, decoded text lines provide information on the relative strength of synchronization, the average signal-to-noise ratio in dB (relative to the noise power in 2500 Hz bandwidth), and **W**, the measured frequency width of the sync signal, in Hz. A symbol following **W** indicates that an adequate level of synchronization has been achieved: * will be displayed for a normal message, and # for a message including the OOO signal report. Two numbers appear at the end of each line. The first number tells whether the soft-decision Reed Solomon decoder failed (0) or succeeded (1). The second number gives a relative confidence level on a 0 to 10 scale for results produced by the Deep Search decoder. Shorthand messages do not produce these numbers.

If a JT65 transmission synchronizes correctly, its spectral information is added into an accumulating array. Subsequent transmissions added into this array can make it possible to decode the average, even if individual transmissions were not decodable. Results of such decoding attempts appear in the Average Text window.

The JT65 Deep Search decoder necessarily has a "grey area" in which it finds a solution but may have only moderate confidence in it. In such cases the decoder appends a "?" to the decoded text, and the operator must make the final decision as to whether the decoding is believable. Be aware that because of the mathematical message structure, incorrect decodings will not differ from the correct one in only a few characters; more likely, they will contain wholly incorrect call signs and grid locators. As you gain experience in recognizing the graphical and numerical indications of proper message synchronization (Sync, dB, DT, DF, W, and the green, red, and blue curves), as well as the effects of birdies and other interference, you will become adept at recognizing and rejecting the occasional false decodes. If it appears that an unexpected (and perhaps exotic) station is calling you, wait until you decode the message again in a subsequent transmission. Random decoding errors will seldom repeat themselves.

Several options are available for adjusting the JT65 decoding procedure to your liking. If you check **Decode | JT65 | Only EME calls**, only a subset of call signs in the database that include an "EME" flag will be used in the Deep Search procedure. Check **"No Shorthands if Tx 1"** if you wish to suppress shorthand decodings when you are still transmitting the first Tx message. The **Decode | JT65** sub-menu offers four options for the Deep Search decoder. The first, **No Deep Search**, disables it entirely. **Normal Deep Search** turns it on but suppresses output with confidence levels less than 3, and **Aggressive Deep Search** allows output down to level 1. The last option, **"Include Average in Aggressive Deep Search,"** applies the Deep Search procedure to the accumulating average as well as the most recently received data. You can check the **Sked** box if you are running a schedule with a known station and do not wish to see any results from the Deep Search decoder that are not relevant to your QSO.

JT65 messages can have one of three basic formats:

1. Two to four alphanumeric fields with specific contents, as described below

2. Any other arbitrary text, up to 13 characters

3. Special shorthand messages RO, RRR, and 73

The four fields of a type 1 message usually consist of two legal call signs, an optional grid locator, and the optional signal report OOO. CQ or QRZ can be substituted for the first call sign. An add-on country prefix followed by "/", a suffix preceded by "/", a signal report of the form "–NN" or "R–NN", or the message fragments "RO", "RRR" or "73" can be substituted for the grid locator. The minus sign in the numerical report is required, and the two-digit number NN must lie between 01 and 30. In circumstances where there could be any confusion about who is sending a report or who it is intended for, these messages including call signs are the preferred method of sending signal reports. A list of the supported add-on country prefixes can be displayed from the **Help** menu.

Messages used in a minimal JT65 QSO are typically something like the following:

1. CQ K1JT FN20

2. K1JT VK7MO QE37

3. VK7MO K1JT FN20 OOO

4. RO

5. RRR

6. 73

In a pile-up situation, messages 3, 4, and 5 might alternatively be sent as:

3. VK7MO K1JT –24

4. K1JT VK7MO R–26

5. VK7MO K1JT RRR

Some other examples of properly formatted JT65 messages include the following:

CQ ZA/PA2CHR

CQ RW1AY/1

ZA/PA2CHR K1JT

K1JT ZA/PA2CHR OOO

QRZ K1JT FN20

The JT65 shorthand messages are powerful because they can be decoded at signal levels some 5 dB below those required for standard messages. (In fact, they can often be decoded by ear, or by eye directly from the SpecJT waterfall display.) If a message starts with RO, RRR, or 73, the shorthand format will be sent. If the message text satisfies the requirements for a type 1 message, the specified call signs, CQ, QRZ, prefix, locator, and/or report will be encoded and sent as entered. With any other entry, 13 characters of arbitrary text will be encoded and sent. The actual message being transmitted is displayed in the bottom right corner of the main screen. Yellow highlighting indicates a standard message, blue a shorthand message, and red a JT65 plain text message.

CW

The *WSJT* CW mode is provided as a convenience for operators attempting EME contacts using timed transmissions of 1, 2, or 2.5 minutes duration. The program sends EME-style messages at 15 WPM by keying an 800 Hz audio tone, and it takes care of the timing and T/R switching. Receiving is left up to you, the operator. Select the desired period by right- or left-clicking on the label at bottom center of the main window. Present conventions typically use 1 minute sequences on 50 MHz, either 1 or 2 minutes on 144 MHz, and 2.5 minutes on 432 MHz and above.

Unlike D-STAR, which is a digital standard devised by and for Amateur Radio, APCO-25 was developed specifically for local, state and federal public safety communications. "APCO" is the Association of Public-Safety Communications Officials, originally an association of police communication technicians, but now a private organization. APCO has a technical standards group responsible for planning the future needs of police (and more recently public-safety) users. It was through this group that a standard for advanced narrow-band digital communications (voice or data) was developed. This standard is known as APCO Project 25, APCO-25, or simply P25.

The overall purpose of the APCO-25 standard is to make it possible for governments to shift from analog to digital communications with the least difficulty possible. This means placing a great deal of emphasis on *backward compatibility* (P25 radios include analog operation and newer P25 technology doesn't render older technology instantly obsolete) and *interoperability* (the ability for all P25 radios to communicate with each other).

In the public safety world, interoperability is a key selling point. The chaotic communications experience in New York City during the September 11, 2001 terrorist attack and in 2005 during Hurricane Katrina demonstrated the critical importance of interoperability. During both disasters there were numerous instances where radio communication between various groups was impossible because each group was using mutually incompatible equipment.

APCO-25 is comprised of a "Suite of Standards" that specifies eight open interfaces between the various components of a land mobile radio system.

■**Common Air Interface** (CAI) standard specifies the type and content of signals transmitted by compliant radios. One radio using CAI should be able to communicate with any other CAI radio, regardless of manufacturer. There is a detailed explanation of the Common Air Interface in Appendix C of this book.

■**Subscriber Data Peripheral Interface** standard specifies the port through which mobiles and portables can connect to laptops or data networks

■**Fixed Station Interface** standard specifies a set of mandatory messages supporting digital voice, data, encryption and telephone interconnect necessary for communication between a Fixed Station and P25 RF Subsystem

■**Console Subsystem Interface** standard specifies the basic messaging to interface a console subsystem to a P25 RF Subsystem

■**Network Management** Interface standard specifies a single network management scheme which will allow all network elements of the RF subsystem to be managed

■**Data Network Interface** standard specifies the RF Subsystem's connections to computers, data networks, or external data sources

■**Telephone Interconnect Interface** standard specifies the interface to Public Switched Telephone Network (PSTN) supporting both analog and ISDN telephone interfaces.

■**Inter RF Subsystem Interface** (ISSI) standard specifies the interface between RF subsystems which will allow them to be connected into wide area networks.

You'll find more details about the APCO-25 standard on the Web at **www.apcointl.org/frequency/project25/index.html**.

APCO-25 "PHASES"

The APCO-25 rollout was planned in "phases." Phase 1 radio systems operate in 12.5 kHz analog, digital or mixed mode. Phase 1 radios use continuous 4-level FM (C4FM) modulation for digital transmissions at 4800 baud and 2 bits per symbol, which yields 9600 bits per second total throughput. It is interesting to note that receivers designed for the C4FM standard can also demodulate the compatible quadrature phase shift keying (CQPSK) standard. The parameters of the CQPSK signal were chosen to yield the same signal deviation at symbol time as C4FM while using only 6.25 kHz of bandwidth. This is to pave the way for Phase 2, which we'll discuss in a moment.

In a typical Phase 1 radio, the analog signal from the microphone is compressed and digitized by an Improved Multi-Band Excitation, or *IMBE*, vocoder. This is a proprietary device licensed by Digital Voice Systems Corporation. The IMBE vocoder converts the voice signal from the microphone into digital data at a rate of 4400 bps. An additional 2400 bps worth of signaling information is added, along with 2800 bps of forward error correction to protect the bits during transmission. The combined channel rate for IMBE in P25 radios is 9600 bps. **Figure 6-1** shows a block diagram of a typical P25 transceiver.

P25 radios are able to operate in analog mode with older analog radios and in digital mode with other P25 radios. If an agency wants to mix old analog radios with P25 radios, the system must use a control channel that both types of radios can understand. That means a trunked radio system.

Phase 1 is the current phase in use at the time this course was written and is likely to be in force for a number of years to come. Phase 2 is still under development. Phase 2 will use the AMBE vocoder, the same one used in D-STAR equipment (this does *not* mean that Phase 2 APCO-25 and D-STAR will be interoperable, however). Phase 2 also involves console interfacing between repeaters and other subsystems, and man-machine interfaces for console operators that would facilitate centralized training, equipment transitions and personnel movement.

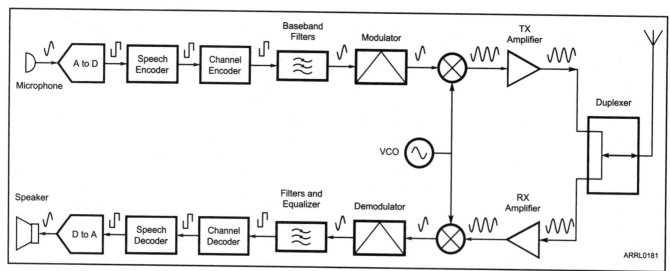

Figure 6-1—Block diagram of a typical P25 transceiver.

OPERATING APCO-25

APCO-25 transceivers vary substantially from one manufacturer to another, but there are some common elements. For example, there are 3 methods to send a voice message, with several options and variations of each case.

■ **Routine Group Call:** This is the most common type of call and is intended for a group of users within the system. This type of call is typically initiated by pressing the Push-To-Talk switch.

■ **Emergency Group Call:** This type of call is similar to a Routine Group Call, but is used during an emergency condition. An emergency condition is defined by the radio system users. This type of call is typically initiated by pressing the **EMERGENCY** switch, which is prominent on every APCO-25 compliant radio.

■ **Individual Call:** This type of call is addressed to a specific individual. The caller enters the subscribers Unit ID and this is used as the Destination ID by the radio making the call. This type of call is made after the Destination ID is entered into the radio. For ham

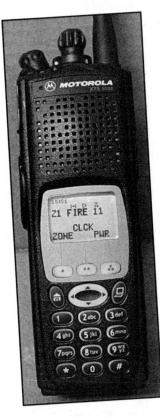

A Motorola handheld P25 transceiver.

application, the Unit and Destination IDs can be call signs.

In addition to data capability, APCO-25 radios and repeater systems also support various control messages. These control messages use packet data to transfer discrete information. For example…

- **Emergency Alarm:** Activated by a user to inform the dispatcher that an emergency is taking place.
- **Call Alert:** Sends a data packet to another user identifying the source of the Call Alert and requesting

the destination station to contact the source. Call Alert is typically used if the destination user did not respond to a voice message from the source.

- **Radio Check:** Used to determine if a specific user is currently available on the radio system. A response to the Radio Check is required, or the system will assume the user is not available.
- **Radio Inhibit (Radio Uninhibit):** Used to deny all calls between the inhibited user. Uninhibit cancels the inhibit status of the user.
- **Status Update and Status Request:** Status Update is used by a user to indicate his or her current status. Status Request is used by a user to request the current status of a another user.
- **Message:** A Message may be sent by a user to the system or to a specific user.
- **Telephone Interconnect Dialing:** If a telephone connection is available through the system, the user can place a call, or someone outside the system can call the user.
- **Radio Unit Monitor:** A form of remote control that will key a user's radio upon request from a central dispatcher so that he or she can listen to activity at the user location.

APCO-25 AND AMATEUR RADIO

At the time this book was written, no one was making APCO-25 transceivers specifically for the Amateur Radio market, but that hasn't stopped some hams from exploring this mode. Because APCO-25 is an open, published standard, it *is* legal for Amateur Radio, but the trick is finding the means to adapt commercial APCO-25 gear to ham purposes.

The present-day Amateur Radio APCO-25 world looks a lot like the analog FM community in the early 1970s. Back then, none of the Amateur Radio manufacturers were making FM transceivers or repeaters. Hams were forced to modify existing commercial FM gear, which typically consisted of transceivers that had seen duty in police cruisers, taxi cabs and so on. Many of the FM "gurus" in those days were individuals who were employed by two-way radio service shops. These hams had easy access not only to test equipment, but also to the knowledge of how to modify commercial transceivers for ham applications. They built the first Amateur Radio FM repeaters by repurposing commercial

Mobile P25 rigs are often supplied with sophisticated microphone units that display user ID, GPS location data and short text messages.

two-way radio transmitters and receivers.

Amateur Radio APCO-25 enthusiasts today are treading the same path taken by analog FM pioneers more than 30 years ago. They are modifying commercial APCO-25 equipment for Amateur Radio and setting up APCO-25 repeater systems. Thanks to online sites such as eBay, it is relatively easy to track down surplus APCO-25 transceivers. Manufactured in both handheld and mobile configurations, these rigs are available for either VHF or UHF.

Modifying commercial APCO-25 radios has become a software hacking game. Since most functions of these radios are software defined, you can change their operating characteristics (including frequencies) with a computer and a compatible interface.

The first step is to obtain the programming software, which can be different for every brand. Some manufacturers provide programming software if you purchase the radio as new equipment.

A MA/COM APCO-25 mobile transceiver.

Others are highly restrictive and will not provide their software under any conditions. Motorola, a popular brand among amateur P25 users, uses different programs for every transceiver model. The programming software must be purchased from them at a cost of $250 to $300. To re-program the Motorola transceivers (as well as many other brands), you may need a hardware device that is sometimes referred to as a Radio Interface Box, or RIB.

The downside of using surplus commercial equipment is that it can be expensive. At the time of this writing, used handheld APCO-25 transceivers were selling for as much as $700 at eBay and other sites. Modified APCO-25 repeaters can cost several thousand dollars.

The cost hurdle hasn't deterred hams from setting up APCO-25 networks. There are more than a dozen amateur APCO-25 repeater system in operation throughout the United States. Many of these repeaters operate in mixed mode—analog and digital. Others are digital only. The ability to operated in mixed modes is one of the strengths of Amateur Radio APCO-25. An APCO-25 repeater, for instance, can support digital voice and data with APCO-25 transceivers, but can still relay analog FM traffic.

More ham-related programming information is available at the following Web sites, although it applies specifically to Motorola transceivers:

■ www.batlabs.com/newbie.html
■ www.batlabs.com/flash.html

AMATEUR APCO-25 IN EMERGENCY APPLICATIONS

APCO-25 transceivers can operate in either analog or digital voice modes. APCO-25 rigs also support selective calling and are capable of sending data within a networked environment.

APCO-25 has potential for use in Amateur Radio emergency communications, although that potential has yet to be tested. Some manufacturers are marketing rapid deployment APCO-25 repeaters, which can be used to set up networks at a moment's notice. Many of these are designed to use solar power.

With a network of portable repeaters in the disaster zone, and possibly long-distance VHF/UHF data links

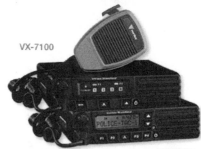

Two Vertex (Yaesu) APCO-25 radios.

VX-7100

VX-7200

to the nearest Internet access point, an Amateur Radio implementation of APCO-25 may provide excellent service.

HIGH SPEED MULTIMEDIA (HSMM) RADIO

By *John Champa, K8OCL*

Any discussion of High Speed Multimedia radio must start with a special communication mode known as *spread spectrum*. Its origins are unusual, to say the least. Rather than springing from the mind of a career scientist or engineer, spread spectrum was the 1940s brainchild of Hollywood movie actress Hedy Lamarr and composer George Antheil. In fact, they were granted a patent for spread spectrum.

In its most basic form, the idea behind spread spectrum is ingenious, yet simple. Instead of a signal appearing on a single frequency, the signal is spread throughout a range of frequencies. In the original frequency hopping spread spectrum design, the signal rapidly switched from one frequency to the other. Spread spectrum turned out to be ideal for military communications (the kind Hedy Lamarr and George Antheil had in mind) because the wide bandwidth signals are difficult to detect using conventional AM/SSB and FM receiving gear. With wide signal bandwidth and low power densities, if anything at all is heard, it is simply perceived as an increase in the background noise level.

Although HSMM has spread spectrum at its heart, HSMM is not a specific mode *per se*. In Amateur Radio it means any VHF/UHF/SHF/EMF digital mode with a raw data rate above 56 kilobits per second (kbps). Accordingly, the D-STAR system discussed earlier in this book is one form of HSMM radio. With existing technology the HSMM data rate provides enough signal capacity to operate more than one mode at the same time. Usually it uses an IP-based transport infrastructure that makes it completely compatible with personal computer (PC) technology.

Despite the fact that John Costas, W2CRR, published a paper on nonmilitary applications of spread spectrum communications in 1959, spread spectrum was used almost solely for military purposes until the late 1970s. In 1981, the Federal Communications Commission (FCC) granted the Amateur Radio Research and Development Corporation (AMRAD) a Special Temporary Authorization (STA) to conduct Amateur Radio spread spectrum experiments.

In June 1986, the FCC authorized all US amateurs to use spread spectrum above 420 MHz. These FCC grants were intended to encourage the development of spread spectrum, which is an important element in commercial wireless systems. An example of such commercial wireless products are wireless local area networks (WLAN) using the Institute of Electrical and Electronics Engineers (IEEE, pronounced "I triple E") radio standards 802.11. In their traditional fashion, radio amateurs have been quick to adapt these commercial products to their needs in radio experimenting.

SPREAD-SPECTRUM TRANSMISSIONS

A transmission can be called "spread spectrum" if the RF bandwidth used is (1) much larger than that needed for traditional modulation schemes and (2) independent of the modulation content. Although numerous spread spectrum schemes are in existence, amateurs can use any of them as long as the modulation scheme has been published, for example, on the ARRLWeb. By far, direct-sequence spread spectrum (DSSS) and orthogonal frequency domain modulation (OFDM) are the most popular forms within the Amateur Radio community. The older frequency hopping spread spectrum (FHSS) has fallen into disuse as cheap used commercial gear becomes less available.

The Global Positioning System (GPS) is an excellent example of the use of DSSS. The average signal at the GPS receiver's antenna terminals is approximately −160 dBw. Since most sources of interference are relatively narrowband, spread-spectrum users will also benefit, as narrowband interfering signals are rejected automatically during the despreading process. These benefits are obtained at the cost of fairly intricate circuitry: The transmitter must spread its signal over a wide bandwidth in accordance with a certain prearranged code, while the receiver must somehow synchronize on this code and recombine the signal.

This technical complexity is offset by several important advantages:

- ■ *Interference rejection*. If the interference is not synchronized with the original spread spectrum signal, it will not appear after despreading at the receiver.
- ■ *Security*. The length and sophistication of the pseudo-random codes used can be such as to make unauthorized recovery difficult, if not impossible.
- ■ *Power density*. Low power density makes for easy hiding of the RF signal and a resulting lower probability of detection.

For the Amateur Radio community particular benefit is derived from the interference rejection, since it offers both robustness and reliability of transmissions, as well as a low probability of interference to other users.

Additionally, spread spectrum has the potential to allow better utilization of the RF spectrum allocated to amateurs.

There is a limit as to how many conventional signals can be placed in a given band before serious transmission degradation takes place. Additional spread spectrum signals will not cause severe interference, but may instead only raise the background noise level. This becomes particularly important in bands shared with other users and in our VHF and UHF bands increasingly targeted by commercial users. The utilization of a channel by many transmitters is essentially the concept behind CDMA (Code Division Multiple Access), a system in which several DSSS transmissions can share the same RF bandwidth, provided they utilize orthogonal pseudo-random sequences.

Amateur Radio Spread Spectrum

In 1989, in a paper titled *License-Free Spread Spectrum Packet Radio*, Al Broscius, N3FCT, suggested the use of Part 15 spread spectrum wireless local area network (WLAN) devices be put to use in Amateur Radio.

Then in late 1999, the FCC considerably relaxed the Amateur Radio service rules regarding the use of spread spectrum. These changes allowed amateurs to use commercial off-the-shelf (COTS) Part 15 spread spectrum devices used under § 97.311 of the FCC rules. The stage was now set for amateur HSMM.

HSMM AND THE EMERGENCE OF COMMERCIAL PART 15 EQUIPMENT

Just as military surplus radio equipment fueled Amateur Radio in the 1950s, and commercial FM radios and repeaters snowballed the popularity of VHF/UHF amateur repeaters in the 1960s and 1970s, the availability of commercial wireless LAN (WLAN) equipment is driving the direction and popularity of Amateur Radio use of spread spectrum in the 2000s.

FCC Part 15 documents the technical rules for commercial spread-spectrum equipment. The IEEE has provided the standards under which manufacturers have developed equipment for sale commercially for unlicensed use. You'll recognize this equipment in the form of wireless routers, access points and more. IEEE 802.11 standardized DSSS (802.11b) and OFDM (802.11g) for the 2.4 GHz band provide data rates of 11 to 54 Megabits per second (Mbit/s), half-duplex. 802.11g, which does not use spread spectrum but uses OFDM for data rates of 6, 9, 12, 18, 24, 36, 48 and 54 Mbit/s, is backward compatible with 802.11b. 802.11a addresses the use of OFDM in certain parts of the 5 GHz band, but unfortunately most of the equipment presently made in the US operates outside the Part 15 shared portion of 5 GHz Amateur Band. 802.11a provides the same data rates as 802.11g. The currently unreleased 802.11n standard promises data rates in excess of 108 Mbit/s.

The Wireless Fidelity (WiFi) organization certifies compliance of manufactures equipment with these FCC Part 15 requirements. Recently, radio amateurs have started to investigate the use of ZigBee (802.15.4) devices for mesh networking capabilities. By trading bandwidth for power output, the ranges of these devices are surprising good. Increasing the power output beyond the Part 15 restrictions may lead to some significant opportunities for radio experimenting under Part 97 of the regulations. That is the reason radio amateurs refer to our use of this equipment under Part 97 as HSMM radio rather than "WiFi", "WiMax" etc. because we, as a licensed radio service, are not bound by such restrictions. However, we have other restrictions which will be mentioned later.

MULTIMEDIA MODES

In HSMM radio we have the opportunity to operate several different modes at the same time, and usually do. Being generally IP-based, and given enough bandwidth, radio amateurs have the capability to do the same things with HSMM radio that are done on the Internet…

AUDIO: Although technically digital voice, since it is two-way voice over an IP (VoIP) network similar to EchoLink and IRLP networks used to link many Amateur Radio repeaters over the Internet.

VIDEO: Motion and color video modes are called amateur digital video (ADV). This is to distinguish it from Digital Amateur Television (DATV). DATV uses hardware digital coder-decoders (CODEC) to achieve relatively high-definition video similar to *entertainment quality TV*. The usual practice in HSMM radio is to use a far less expensive (often free) PC-based software video CODEC such as Microsoft *Netmeeting* to achieve *video communications quality* signals in much smaller bandwidths.

TEXT: Text exchanges via a keyboard are often used in HSMM radio, but they are similarly called by their Internet or packet radio name: *Chat mode*. If a server is available on the network, e-mail can also be exchanged.

IMAGE: File transfers using file transfer protocol (FTP) e.g., JPEG, can also be done, just as on the Internet.

MOTION VIDEO: FTP of MPEG files can provide one-way video streaming of short video clips. Alternatively, if your Hinternet has an I-Gateway or server, you can simply send a link (URL).

REMOTE CONTROL (RC): Individual devices or even complete stations can be remotely controlled.

WARNING: Do not use two computers in ad hoc mode for remote station operation. This method is completely insecure. You must use an AP/wireless router for the host and a wireless client adaptor in the far end PC as a client. This will allow for implementation of various network infrastructure security measures to protect the link. More on this later.

MESH NETWORKS: A main emphasis in HSMM radio is a dramatic shift in emphasis within Amateur Radio from traditional analog point-to-point radio connections and toward *networked digital radios*. This has resulted in many amateurs nick naming HSMM radio *The Hinternet*. Although the name may imply an under-dog status, the intent is to provide a radio amateur based network completely independent of the Internet. Is this really possible? Won't it always be necessary to use the Internet for at least part of any high-speed radio amateur networking infrastructure? Not necessarily. Already we are seeing trends in Automatic Position Reporting Systems (APRS), Automatic Link Establishment (ALE), etc. in which all the radios are networked together most of the time.

HSMM RADIO APPLICATIONS

By far the most intense application of HSMM radio technology has been in Field Day activities. Field Day presents a special challenge since the event is intended to simulate emergency operating. Field Day stations are usually outdoors and operate with limited resources.

Field Day HSMM applications generally fall into two easy and economical areas, but there undoubtedly are many others:
- Providing a radio local area network (RLAN) covering several acres of radio stations.
- Providing a high-speed (HS) data link back to another amateur's house where there is a DSL line or cable modem for an HSMM Internet Gateway.

In the more sophisticated Field Day operations, we see both applications being served. Why? With the RLAN logging can be instantaneous and, for example, duplicate contacts can be immediately identified and eliminated. With access to an RLAN server, ongoing scoring can be accomplished. This allows the leadership to frequently analyze the group's performance. They can then quickly re-direct resources and activities on the run to better achieve the club's objectives.

Having an HS data link to the outside world from a remote Field Day location allows sending e-mail, photos, and other material to other club members joining the Field day after the start-up or wanting to watch and learn. Also, supporting individuals and family members can be kept informed of needed supplies and situational changes complete with images, etc.

Shared High-Speed Internet Access

Sharing high-speed Internet access (cable, DSL, etc) with another radio amateur is not a frequent application for HSMM radio, but there is an occasional call for it, usually not for routine use, but for special events. Remember that half of the US population is restricted to slow dial-up Internet connections (usually around 20 to 40 kbit/s) over regular analog telephone lines. Getting a high-speed Internet connection, even a shared one, can dramatically change the surfing experience! Just remember that if you use an HSMM radio to share HS access to the Internet, Amateur Radio has content restrictions. For example, you cannot use the link to run your business, transmit music, etc.

What about pop-up ads? These can be effectively blocked, but if one slips through it is analogous to an amateur television station (ATV) transmitting an outdoor scene (e.g., Memorial Day parade) and inadvertently picking-up a billboard in the station camera. Such background sources are merely incidental to your transmission and can be ignored. They are not the primary purpose of your communications, plus they are not intended for rebroadcast to the public, making them totally unrelated to your transmissions.

Remember when sharing Internet access that some cable and DSL companies do not permit such sharing of their services. Other companies seem not to care. It is better to check out the customer agreement situation first. Different ISPs (Internet Service Providers) have different agreements. The control operator of the host HSMM radio node or I-Gate (Internet gateway), is responsible is responsible for ensuring compliance with the user agreement.

Security for all HSMM radios and their associated computer needs to be emphasized here:

■ All PCs must have an individual or personal firewall, either software or hardware.
■ All PCs must have an active and updated anti-spyware/anti-virus software program(s).
■ Always be a safe computer user whether you are on the Internet or the Hinternet. Protect your system!
■ This topic is covered in additional detail in the section on Information Security that follows.

Figure 7-1—The MFJ-1800 is an inexpensive Yagi antenna designed for HSMM on 2.4 GHz.

Gaming Over HSMM Radio

Just as on the Internet, it is possible to do such things as playing interactive games using HSMM radio. Currently individuals play chess via CW (continuous wave telegraphy) on the HF (high frequency/shortwave) ham bands. The big difference is, with HSMM radio the game can come complete with sound effects and full-motion animation. This can be lots of fun for new and old hams alike. Further, it can attract others in the "Internet Generation" to become interested in Amateur Radio and perhaps become new radio club members. In the future it is easy to imagine entire radio amateur clubs based on gaming technology much as clubs presently are often focused on contesting. In the commercial gaming world these activities are called "WLAN Parties." Such e-games are also an excellent method for testing the true speed of your station's Hinternet link capability.

HSMM Radio in Emergency Communications

There are a number of significant reasons and exciting new examples why HSMM radio might be the way of the future for many Emergency Communications (EmComm) situations.

These may or may not be under ARES, RACES, or MARS auspices.

1. The amount of digital radio traffic on 2.4 GHz is increasing and operating under low powered, unlicensed Part 15 limitations cannot overcome this noise.

2. EmComm organizations increasingly need high-speed radio networks that can simultaneously handle voice, video, data and text traffic.

3. The cost of a commercially installed HS

data network can be more than emergency organizations and communities can collectively afford. The volunteers and HSMM radio operators can be a stop gap measure to provide such community assistance until a commercially available solution can be provided.

4. EmComm managers also know that they need to continuously exercise any emergency communications system and have trained operators for the system in order for it to be dependable.

Being able to communicate what is taking place at a disaster site to everybody on the HSMM radio network can be invaluable in estimating the severity of the situation, planning appropriate responding resources and other reactions. The Emergency Operations Center (EOC) can actually see what is happening

Figure 7-2--N5OOM and the North Texas Microwave Society have used RooTenna-based systems for public service activities. The RooTenna is the square housing atop the support mast.

while it is happening. Submitting a written report while simultaneously talking to the EOC using Voice over IP (VoIP) would provide additional details.

Prior to connecting any HSMM radio device to any EOC internal data network, however, the control operator must coordinate with and get approval from the appropriate EOC officials. All EOCs and other governmental facilities (National Guard, etc.) have strict security policies regarding the connection of any wireless devices to their wired data network.

With HSMM radio, often all that is needed to accomplish such immediacy in the field is a laptop computer equipped with a wireless local area network card (PCMCIA) with an external antenna jack, a small directive 2.4 GHz antenna such as the MFJ-1800 (see **Figure 7-1**), an antenna stand, and an inexpensive webcam or even the video output from a digital camera. Other creative approaches are possible, such as the Pacific Wireless RooTenna (**www.pacwireless.com**), a small radio housing with a built in 19 dB antenna. N5MOO and the North Texas Microwave Society have used RooTenna-based systems for public service activities (see **Figure 7-2**.)

HSMM RADIO RELAYS

There are a number of ways to extend an HSMM radio link. The most obvious means would be to run higher power (at both ends of the link) and to place the antennas as high as possible (**Figure 7-3**), as is the case with VHF/UHF FM repeaters. Even in densely populated urban areas of the country this approach with 802.11, at least in the 2.4 GHz band, may cause some interference with non-licensed other users. Although the law states that such uses must tolerate interference from licensed users of the band, it is best to avoid it. Radio amateurs should always strive to be good neighbors.

There are several simple means of accomplishing non-interference with Part 15ers. First, is by doing an RF site survey of the area and the route you wish to cover. NetStumbler (**www.netstumbler.com**) is an excellent a free radio tool that

Figure 7-3—Height is important for any HSMM installation. In this photo, Daryl, KG4PRR, is installing an HSMM parabolic dish antenna at the home of K4RBZ.

can be used for this purpose. You will also need some quality topographical maps of the route. Secondly, avoid channels already in use as much as possible, remembering that only channels 1 through 6 are within the amateur band. Thirdly, use highly directive antennas at both ends of the link. Follow good radio amateur operating practices and use the minimum power necessary to complete the link. When running high power (anything over a few hundred milliwatts) use adequate filtering to avoid splattering by suppressing the signal sidebands of the channel you are using, etc.

There is a quick short cut to conducting the ranging portion of an RF site survey. You want to see beforehand see if the path you have in mind might be suitable. Try using two 1.2 GHz handheld transceivers. If possible, get at the same height as the directive antennas you are going to use, and see if any contact whatsoever is possible. Chances are fair that if the 1 or more Watts of 1.2 GHz FM signal does not get through, then neither will the 2.4 GHz link signal without some special attention to design.

Other means of getting greater distances using 802.11 on 2.4 GHz or other amateur bands should also be considered. One approach we have already mentioned: Use highly directive, high-gain antennas, or what is called the directive link approach.

Another approach used by some HSMM radio networks is what is called a low-profile radio network design. They depend on several low power sources and radio relays of various types. For example, two HSMM radio repeaters (known commercially as *access points (AP) or wireless routers*) may be placed back-to-back in what is known as bridge mode. In this configuration they will simply act as an automatic radio relay for the high-speed data. Using a series of such radio relays on a series of amateur towers between the end-points of the link, it is possible to cover greater distances with relatively low power. Although the data throughput will suffer to some extent using this approach, the link will still move lots of multimedia data.

A BASIC HSMM RADIO STATION

How do you set up an HSMM radio base station? It is really very easy. HSMM radio amateurs can go to any electronics outlet or office supply store and buy commercial off the shelf (COTS) Wireless LAN gear, either IEEE 802.11b (now more or less obsolete and usually sold for very low prices) or IEEE 802.11g.

The favorite location for radio amateurs to shop is Freeman, Anderson, and Bird (FAB Corp) where most of the personnel are radio amateurs and if you identify yourself as an HSMM radio buff you can get a 10% discount (**www.fab-corp.com**). More importantly, being radio amateurs, they can give you technical advice on how to most economically and effectively accomplish your HSMM radio experimenting objectives.

The most popular model in use in Amateur Radio by far is the Linksys WRT54GL wireless router (**Figure 7-4**). It is a combination unit consisting of a wireless access point (AP) or hub coupled with a router. As with other routers, your host PC or laptop connects directly to it using a standard Ethernet cable. If the PC is also connected to the Internet, then it may also perform the function of a *gateway*. If further, this PC is loaded with appropriate server software, it may also perform a network server function such a se-mail management.

This HSMM radio popular wireless router is a *Linux* based model that supports firmware upgrades to distros such as DD-WRT and Tomato (see this URL for more details: **www.youtube.com/watch?v=No_NyW2Ug9o**).

The WRT54GL Router

Linksys released the WRT54GL in 2005 to support third-party firmware based on *Linux*, after the original WRT54G line was switched from *Linux* to VxWorks. See **Table 7-1**.

The first step in configuring your router for HSMM is to

disconnect both rubber duck antennas that came with the unit and put them in your parts box or nearest trash container! To connect any outside antenna or a small field antenna such as the MFJ-1800 mentioned earlier, you are going to be become familiar with RP (reverse polarity) connectors. These are connectors that may appear to be male connectors on the outside. However, a close examination of the interior of the connector will reveal that there is no pin. Instead it will be equipped with a socket. Confusing? Not really. These RP connectors are used by the manufacturers to discourage Part 15 owners from using the equipment in ways for which it was not WiFi certified. Being licensed radio amateurs; we are not bound by such certification and can modify the system to accomplish our specific requirements.

How do you get around this situation so you can connect your coaxial cable for the long run out to the tower, mast pipe, roof, etc? There are two common approaches. (1) use a TNC RP to female N-series adaptor, or (2) construct or purchase a pig tail adaptor with a TNC RP connector on one end and a female N-series connector on the other end.

There are often two antenna ports on wireless devices. These are used for *receive* space diversity. The wireless device will normally automatically select whichever antenna is receiving the best signal at any specific moment. Which do you connect to?

The transmitted signal from the wireless router always goes out the same antenna port. It does not switch. In other words, except for some Cisco models, most wireless devices have *only receive space diversity*. They do not have transmit space diversity. Some access points/wireless routers will allow you to manually (via software) select the antenna port that is used for transmission. When it does not allow such a choice, you will need to find some means of detecting which antenna is the transmit antenna port with RF output power present. That is the port to be used for the pig tail or feed line connection to your exterior antenna. Space diversity is discussed in more detail later.

Now you are ready to connect your wireless router to the length of low-loss coaxial cable (often Times LMR-400, equivalent or better) running to the tower, mast pipe, or roof mounted directive antenna outside. You now have the host end of the link.

Software Configuration

Linksys is the most popular 802.11 modulation AP/wireless router presently used in HSMM radio; the comments here apply generally to that brand and similar units from other manufacturers. If you use another brand of AP/wireless router, follow the instructions from that manufacturer. The usual practice is to use the supplied Linksys CD as a nice Frisbee to play with your puppy. Most people just use the wireless network configuration tool that comes with their PC's OS (operating system), especially if it is *Microsoft XP*, which works particularly well.

Figure 7-4--The Linksys WRT54GL wireless router.

Table 7-1

LinkSys WRT54GL Routers Supporting Third-Party Firmware

Version	CPU Clock	RAM	Flash Memory	Prefix S/N	Notes
1.0	200 MHz	16 MB	4 MB	CL7A	New model line, released after the version 5 WRT54G, which returns to a *Linux*-based OS as opposed to the VxWorks firmware. SpeedBooster is not enabled in stock firmware; however, third-party firmware will enable the feature. The hardware is essentially the same as the WRT54G version 4.0. One alteration is that the internal numbering scheme of the 4-port switch changed in this model, from 1 2 3 4, to 3 2 1 0.
1.1	200 MHz	16 MB	4 MB	CL7B CL7C	In June 20, 2006, this version was shipping with firmware revision 4.30.7. This pre-loaded firmware allows the user to upload a 4MB firmware image, whereas the pre-loaded firmware on version 1.0 limited the image to 3MB. Firmware version 4.30.11 is now available for both hardware versions. Fully supported by Tomato, openwrt, and DD-WRT.
1.1	200 MHz	32 MB	8 MB	CO61	This T-Mobile SPECIAL EDITION is a WRT-54GL (Renamed WRT54G-TM). Uses BCM5352EKPBG Chipset, SpeedBooster technology, & *Linux* OS. Fully supported by Tomato, openwrt, and DD-WRT. It requires a jtag cable to flash a wrt54gl 1.1 cfe to it as its stock cfe will reject non t-mobile/linksys firmware images. Build the cfe from scratch with your router's MAC address using "skynet repair kit." after flashing the cfe to it you can download the Linksys stock firmware for a wrt54gl 1.0 and then use the Linksys Web page update tool to flash the 3rd party firmware onto it. the IP address will go from 192.168.0.1 (t-mobile firmware) to 192.168.1.1(wrt54gl 1.0-1.1 firmware); other third-party firmware unknown

However, I recently installed a Linksys Wireless Print Server on my network so that all the other stations could share my printer without anyone, including me, being physically connected to the device (with the price of ink cartridges you'd better exercise care here!). In that case, the Linksys CD worked perfectly, so you must be your own judge. The point is, be prepared to use other drivers when needed and available, just as you might with any other electronic device in your PC network, wired or wireless. Some of these have the newest drivers and some have the original that came with the unit years ago. They all probably still work to a certain extent.

SSID: The AP/wireless router host software is provided with an *SSID* (Service Set Identifier) that many Part 15 stations turned off for somewhat higher security. But radio amateurs should leave it ON. Enter your call sign as the SSID and use it for the station identification. It constantly broadcasts your call, thus providing automatic and constant station identification. There are 32 characters available for use in this field so more information such as your group's name can be entered too, including spaces and punctuation. If the router asks if you want to enable the broadcast, click **YES**. (Note that SSID in the HSMM world has a somewhat different meaning than SSID in the packet radio community. Among packet users, SSID is defined as Secondary Station Identifier.)

ESSID: Some manufacturers use this term in place of SSID to put emphasis on the fact that the SSID is the name for your *network,* not for a specific wireless AP/router.

ACCESS POINT NAME: When this field is made available (by default it is blank) it is for you to enter a description. This may be handy if you have deployed more than one AP in your network all with your call sign as the SSID. It would allow you to tell them apart. Otherwise, just leave it blank.

CHANNEL: To be as non-interfering with other services as possible, we need to also look at channel selection. The channels provided under Part 15 are only 5 MHz wide. However, the 802.11b/g bandwidth is approximately 20 MHz wide resulting in considerable frequency overlap. Consequently, there are only three totally non-overlapping channels: 1, 6 and 11. Channel 7 and above are outside the Amateur Radio band, so we will focus our discussion only on channels 1 through 6.

After you have completed a site survey of 802.11 activities in your area, you will be in a much better position to select an appropriate channel for your HSMM radio link. In the interim, here are some general guidelines: Avoid channel 6. It is the most common manufacturer default channel setting and 80% or more of your neighbors will be using it for their household wireless LAN. Channel 1 is used by most of the remaining manufactures as their default channel, so that should probably be avoided also. The result is most radio amateurs use channels 3 or 4 depending whether there is a WISP (wireless Internet service provider) operating in their area. Often a WISP will use one of these intermediate channels with a highly directive antenna for

HSMM Glossary

Ad Hoc Mode—An operating mode of a wireless client that allows it to associate directly with any other wireless client without having to go through an Access Point (AP)/Router. See *Infrastructure Mode*.

AP—Access Point (most often now combined with an IP router).

Association—The service used to establish access point/ station mapping and enable station use of the WLANs services in the infrastructure mode.

Authentication—The Process by which the wireless communications system verifies the identity of a user attempting to use a WLAN prior to the user associating with the AP.

COTS—Commercial Off The Shelf equipment.

DHCP—Dynamic Host Configuration Protocol. A protocol used by a client computer to obtain an IP address for use on a network.

HSMM (High Speed Multimedia)—A digital radio communication technique often using spread spectrum modes primarily to simultaneously send and receive video, voice, text and data.

IEEE—Institute of Electrical and Electronic Engineering

IEEE 802.11—An IEEE standard specifying FHSS, DSSS, and OFDM modulation in the 2.4 GHz band

IEEE 802.11a—An IEEE standard specifying OFDM in the 5.8 GHz band at 6, 12, 16, 24, 36, 48, and 54 Mbit/s data rates.

IEEE 802.11b—An IEEE standard specifying DSSS in the 2.4 GHz band at 5.5 and 11 Mbit/s data rates in addition to being backward compatible with DSSS at 1 and 2 Mbit/s specified in 802.11.

IEEE 802.11g—An IEEE standard specifying OFDM in the 2.4 GHz band 6, 12, 16, 24, 36, 48, and 54 Mbit/s data rates in addition to being backward compatible with DSSS at 1, 2, 5.5, and 11 Mbit/s specified in 802.11b.

IEEE 802.11n—An IEEE standard specifying data rates up to 250 Mbit/s and being backward compatible with 802.11a and 802.11g.

IEEE 802.16—An IEEE standard specifying wireless last-mile broadband access in the Metropolitan Area Network (MAN). Also known as WiMax.

ISM—Industrial, Scientific, and Medical. Specific frequency bands authorized by Part 18 rules for non-communication equipment such as microwave ovens, RF lighting, etc. The ISM spectrum where spread spectrum is allowed is located at 2.4 – 2.5 GHz and 5.725 – 5.875 GHz band.

Infrastructure Mode—An operating mode of a client station that requires all communications to go through an Access Point.

OFDM—Orthogonal Frequency Division Multiplexing. A modulation method in which the communication channel is divided into multiple subcarriers each being individually modulated. While not meeting the Part 2 definition of spread spectrum the FCC has given specific authorization for OFDM systems.

Orthogonal—A mathematical term derived from the Greek word *orthos*, which means straight, right or true. In terms of RF, orthogonal applies to the frequencies of the subcarriers which are selected so that at each one of these subcarrier frequencies, all the other subcarriers do not contribute to the overall waveform. In other words, the subcarrier channel is independent of the other channels.

PCMIA—Personal Computer Manufacturer Interface Adaptor. In wireless configurations this is the radio transceiver. This device is now most often simply called the PC card.

Pigtail—A short piece of small diameter, very flexible, low-loss coaxial cable with appropriate connectors on the end(s) to match the PC card antenna port to an external antenna system such as a small dish, etc.. Also called a strain relief cable. Sometimes these are also used for supplying a 2.5 or 5 GHz antenna connection.

RLAN—Radio Local Area Network. These are generally much larger than a WLAN, for example covering an entire Field Day site over many acres, but smaller than a RMAN which might cover an entire town.

RMAN—Radio Metropolitan Area Network

RWAN—Radio Wide Area Network. Regional or even national coverage.

Spread Spectrum (SS)—An information bearing communications system in which: (1) Information is conveyed by modulation of a carrier by some conventional means, (2) the bandwidth is deliberately widened by means of a spreading function over that which would be needed to transmit the information alone.

SSID—Service Set Identifier. A unique alphanumeric string used to identify a WLAN. In HSMM radio this is most often the individual call sign and perhaps the name of the Amateur Radio club or repeater group.

ESSID—See SSID above. The name of your network, not just the device.

UNII—Unlicensed National Information Infrastructure. The UNII spectrum is located at 5.15 - 5.35 GHz, 5.725 - 5.825 GHz, and the recently added 5.470-5.725 GHz band.

USB—Universal Serial Bus.

VPN—Virtual Private Network.

WEP—Wired Equivalent Privacy. An encryption algorithm used by the authentication process for authenticating users and for encrypting data payloads over a WLAN.

WEP Key—An alphanumeric character string used to identify an authenticating station and used as part of the data encryption algorithm.

Wi-Fi—Wireless Fidelity. Refers to products certified as compatible by the Wi-Fi Alliance. See **www.wi-fi. org**. This term is also applied in a generic sense to mean any 802.11 capability operated under FCC regulations Part 15.

WiMax—Familiar name for the IEEE 802.16 standard.

WISP—Wireless Internet Service Provider

WLAN—Wireless Local Area Network.

WPA—WiFi Protected Access methodology used to enhance the network protection issues of encryption and authentication over the use the older WEP algorithm.

back-haul or other purposes. If so, you may wish to coordinate with the WISP and arrange to use some other channel rather than the one specifically used by the WISP. It is not a perfect solution because of all the overlap, but it is a good faith effort to keep most of your stronger signal out of anyone's home, business or governmental WLAN traffic. Yes, we are licensed and they are not, but the political reality is we must learn how to share the band. Radio amateurs have done it successfully on other bands such as 60 meters. We can learn to do it here, too.

WEP: This stands for Wired Equivalent Privacy. In spite of all the horror stories you may have read in the press, this encryption method is more than adequate means to economically achieve authentication and thus keep the vast majority of free-loaders off your network. If you live in the country you may not need to enable this capability. However, in an urban environment, it is probably a good thing to do so that you need not constantly monitor every bit of traffic coming over the network to ensure that it originates from an Amateur Radio station. Mixing traffic with another service that shares the same frequency band is not a generally accepted practice except in times of emergency. Therefore it is often necessary for HSMM radio stations to encrypt their transmissions. *This is not to obscure the meaning of the transmission because the encryption algorithm is standardized and published, and the encryption key is available at any time from the transmitting station. The purpose of the encryption is for authentication and protection of the Part 97 network, not obscuring the meaning. Other forms of authentication often involve a level of complexity that is alien to HSMM radio networks. Most of these networks at this time do not have servers on them. In addition other methods of authentication involve an actual exchange (pass word, user id, etc.) with the Part 15 in order to operate. As mentioned earlier, under normal circumstances (non-emergencies) different services are not intended by the FCC to communicate with one another.*

Why use encryption when the primary purpose is authentication, these are two separate network protection issues? HSMM radio networks, at this stage in the development of the *Hinternet* (the radio amateur version of the Internet) are very simple networks.

Using the onboard encryption to also provide authentication is a readily available, economic and easy way for radio amateurs to protect their HSMM radio network, much as in the manner of FM repeater codes used to protect that type of system. Often clubs handle the WEP/WPA keys in the same manner as PL (Private Line, a Motorola term for limiting access to a repeater by requiring a sub-audio tone code on the incoming transmissions in order to activate the repeater's receiver). See the sidebar "Authentication and HSMM Networks" by Nate Duehr, WYØX, for a fuller explanation as to why radio amateurs often need to use encryption to achieve the one function that is actually needed, i.e., authentication.

However, because we are operating licensed HSMM radio, not unlicensed WiFi, and we have much greater communications capability in terms of antenna design, output power (up to 100 W for spread spectrum modulation), we must follow certain

HSMM Radio References

- Use of HSMM radio within Amateur Radio is a developing story. You can keep up with developments by visiting the Web site of the North Texas Microwave Society: **ntms-hsmm@yahoogroups.com**
- For more details about using HSMM radio for remote control of stations, see the article "Remote-Control HF Operation over the Internet," by Brad Wyatt, K6WR, *QST*, November 2001 p 47-48.
- For guidelines on using e-games on-the air in Amateur Radio, see the HSMM column titled "Is (sic) All Data Acceptable Data" by Neil Sablatzky, K8IT, in the Fall 2003 issue of *CQ VHF*.
- For more information regarding HSMM radio on future OSCAR satellites, visit **www.amsat.org**.
- Burger, Michael W, AH7R, and John J. Champa, K8OCL, "HSMM in a Briefcase," *CQ VHF*, Fall 2003, p 32.
- Champa, John, K8OCL, and Ron Olexa, KA3JIJ, "How To Get Into HSMM," *CQ VHF*, Fall 2003.
- Duntemann, Jeff, K7JPD, *Jeff Duntemann's Wi-Fi Guide,* 2nd Ed, Paraglyph Press, 2004.
- Flickenger, Rob, *Building Wireless Community Networks,* 2nd Ed, O'Reilly, 2003. (Available from the ARRL Book Store).
- Fordham, David, KD9LA, "802.11 Experiments in Virginia's Shenandoah Valley," *QST, July 2005*.
- Gast, Matthew S., *802.11 Wireless Networks, The Definitive Guide*, O'Reilly, 2002. (Available from the ARRL Book Store).
- Mraz, Kris I, N5KM, "High Speed Multimedia Radio," *QST*, April 2003, pp 28-34.
- Olexa, Ron, KA3JIJ, "Wi-Fi for Hams Part 1: Part 97 or Part 15," *CQ*, June 2003, pp 32-36.
- Olexa, Ron, KA3JIJ, "Wi-Fi for Hams Part 2: Building a Wi-Fi Network," *CQ*, July 2003, p 34-38.
- Rinaldo, Paul L., W4RI, and Champa, John J., K8OCL, "On The Amateur Radio Use of IEEE 802.11b Radio Local Area Networks," *CQ VHF*, Spring 2003, p 40-42.
- Rotolo, Don, N2IRZ, "A Cheap and Easy High-Speed Data Connection," *CQ*, February 2003, p 61-64.
- Rotolo, Don, N2IRZ, "Computers & Internet, Building a Decent RF Network", *CQ* 2005, October, p. 66.
- Rotolo, Don, N2IRZ, "Computers & Internet, Digital Connection: Wireless Local Area Network (LAN) Design", *CQ* 2006, December, p. 52.
- Rotolo, Don, N2IRZ, "Packet/Digital, Can HSMM Find a Real Home In Ham Radio? Plus More On RSQ", *CQ* 2005, April, p. 72.
- Rotolo, Don, N2IRZ, "Packet/Digital, Digital Connection: Data encryption is legal!" *CQ* 2006, August, p. 50.

Authentication and HSMM Networks

By Nate Duehr, WYØX

In Amateur Radio digital networks, we often find ourselves in the difficult situation of needing to meet FCC law stated in Part 97.113: Prohibited Transmissions. Where "messages encoded for the purpose of obscuring their meaning except as otherwise provided herein" are not allowed, we are also trying to keep non-Amateur-licensed users from accessing our networks, either accidentally or maliciously.

What amateurs need is a secured form of authentication (likely using encryption keys to encrypt the authentication headers on each packet/ frame of data), but not "payload/message encryption".

Amateurs in recent on-line discussions have pointed out that the IPSec standard allows for this type of partially encrypted packet structure which leaves the packet's payload unencrypted, while encrypting the packet header, but IPSec is not widely deployed in most IPv4 networks today. There are also no consumer-grade inexpensive 802.11 devices which can authenticate based solely on received IPSec packets.

To describe one of the dissenting viewpoints, many amateurs believe that the header information of the packet is still part of the overall "message" intended to be sent by the originating Amateur station. They believe that since part of the transmitter's signal is encrypted, the meaning of the overall message being sent is partially obscured.

Amateurs have debated numerous methods of keeping non-amateurs from joining their 802.11 networks accidentally or maliciously, and thus causing their stations to transmit under indirect control of an unlicensed person.

Many amateurs rely on filtering or blocking non-amateur traffic from unknown MAC addresses. This is ineffective since MAC addresses are sent in the clear in unsecured modes, and they can easily be "spoofed" by anyone to gain access to your amateur-based network. It offers no security at all from packet-sniffing/ snooping technology, available for free on the Internet.

Hash algorithms have also been recommended in online forums as a way to authenticate sessions using passphrases or other information to feed through the hash, producing a mathematically significant outcome that's reproducible using the same passphrase later on. The passphrase would only known to the two station operators, but again hashes are insecure because they're transmitted "in the clear" and are capable of being spoofed, once received.

Some have recommended only accessing things via HTTPS, not fully understanding that HTTPS is just HTTP (the main protocol that Web browsers utilize), which has been encapsulated inside of SSL/TLS (Secure Sockets Layer), a fully-encrypted streaming protocol, thus obscuring the entire message.

In all cases I've seen so far, there are no proposals that work with off-the-shelf equipment, and that don't have to rely on some form of encryption during at least some portion of the on-air packet sequences. Some portion of every packet must still be encrypted.

Since the security/encryption protocols in modern 802.11 APs already exist, are standardized, well-tested, and work between vendors, many HSMM Amateur Radio operators believe it is simply easier to encrypt the entire session.

Part 97.305(c)(3) appears to give us a way to use encrypted sessions, if we're willing to store the transmitted packets from our station. Packet capture of all transmitted traffic and storage of our digital station transmissions is relatively simple today, with the relatively low prices of computer media storage devices and recordable media.

It also seems reasonable to provide a copy of the network encryption key(s) to FCC on-demand, or to any other licensed radio amateur who wishes to monitor and/or join the network, for monitoring purposes, can be done immediately in real-time. If a station refuses to offer up their network key, they could be asked to cease transmission or restrict operation, as described in 97.305(c)(1) and (2).

The encryption debate will continue as long as radio amateurs continue to experiment. Realistically, the only high-confidence method of authenticating nodes or users participating in any on-air digital systems on an untrusted "public" network is via the utilization of modern encryption technology.

practices before using any encryption:

- Use only frequencies above 50 MHz
- Permit no international traffic
- Station identification must be at required times and always in the clear (not encrypted)
- The encryption algorithm used (WEP, WPA, etc.) must be a published algorithm
- Specific key(s) used by the HSMM radio station must be recorded in the station logbook
- All other restrictions regarding the nature of the Amateur Radio traffic apply (no music, etc.)

Most wireless routers will allow for the use of multiple WEP keys, typically up to four. This will allow you to configure the device so that different client stations have different access authority. For example, club members may have one level of access, while visiting radio amateurs may be given a lesser access. Most HSMM radio groups have just one WEP key and everybody gets that one. It is treated in the same fashion, and for much the same purpose, as a repeater's PL tone.

Remember that when it comes to the length of the WEP or other key used, our main purpose is to provide a simple and economical means of authentication already available on the wireless devices. In other words, it is to ensure that only Part 97 stations and not Part 15 stations auto-associate or auto-connect with our

HSMM radio node. The shorter the WEP key, the better! This makes it easy to use and remember. During early HSMM radio experimenting at the turn of the century the shortest possible key (5 characters) was used: HSMM-

AUTHENTICATION TYPE: Some routers will ask for the type of authentication you want to use such as *shared key*, *open system*, and *both*. Click on **shared key** because you will be sharing the WEP/WPA key with any and all radio amateurs who wish to access your HSMM radio node.

DHCP: Some routers will ask if you want Dynamic Host Configuration Protocol enabled. This is the function that assigns IP addresses. Unless you have another source of the DHCP function on your network, you will want to **ENABLE** this function.

ANTENNA SELECTION: A few wireless routers with dual antennas will ask you select an antenna. The default is normally receive space diversity. Because we are going to connect an outside gain antenna, you want to make a selection. Otherwise, you will need to identify which antenna is the actual transmit antenna and connect the feed line to that port.

MAC ADDRESS FILTER: Some wireless routers will allow for this security measure, but it is troublesome to administer it, so it is recommended that you not bother enabling this function. Use WEP or some other method of encryption using the guidelines discussed previously.

OUTPUT POWER: Some wireless routers will allow you to set this power level, often up to 100 mW. As with all other radio amateur operations use only the minimum power needed to accomplish your mission.

If you have selected the Linksys WRT54GL as your host computer's device, this link will help talk you through the set-up: **www.youtube.com/watch?v=No_NyW2Ug9o.**

The Far End of the Link

Next we will address the client end of the link. See **Figure 7-5**. The core of the other end of the HSMM radio link is a computer-operated HSMM 2.4 GHz radio transceiver or simply a PC client adapter. It will probably cost well under $80, especially if you are able to find some older 802.11b cards. A friend of mine, Randy Dunning, KC5QHH, recently purchased one of these PC card transceivers at a flea market for only $5, yet it runs a mighty 200 mW of RF transmitter output power and has a reasonably good quality receiver.

These transceivers/wireless adapter cards usually come in three forms:

(1) One form is called a PC cards as described above. Earlier these were called PCMCIA cards, but more recent terminology

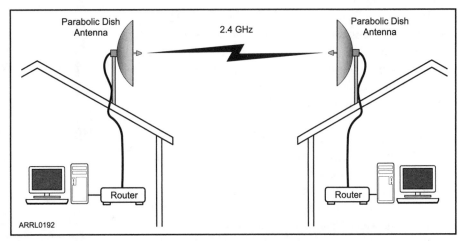

Figure 7-5—This is a simplified diagram of a typical HSMM link between two stations. Note that high gain parabolic dish antennas are being used in this example.

is to simply call them laptop PC cards.

(2) Another type of transceiver/adaptor comes with a USB interface. This is often considered a superior interface for most HSMM stations. The reason for this has nothing to do with the quality of the transceiver, but rather the fragile nature of the tiny connectors (MMCX, etc.) that are found on the PC cards. They are not really designed for frequent plugging and unplugging. Without extreme care, they can be easily torn out. An example of a wireless USB adapter is shown in **Figure 7-6**.

(3) Linksys and other manufactures also produce similar cards for the expansion slot on the rear of your desktop PC too. For example, the Linksys Wireless-G PCI Adapter WMP54G shown in **Figure 7-7**.

Just make certain that regardless of which model client card or type of USB or expansion port interface you purchase has an antenna that is removable or has an external antenna port of some type!

(4) If you are not afraid to modify your laptop, you can access the wireless adaptor built into many new laptops and add a small SMA connector. See **http://repair4laptop.org/ wireless_lan_antenna.html**.

Figure 7-6—This 802.11 b/g Wireless LAN USB Adapter features an external RP-SMA female connector if you wanted to extend its range with an optional antenna. Transmit power is a standard 15dBm It is perfect to travel with and it is the size of a removable USB Thumb Drive, so you can keep it in your pocket!

To connect to the AP/wireless router in an HSMM radio network the wireless computer user(s) at the far end must exit ad-hoc mode and enter what is called the *infrastructure mode*, in their operating software. Infrastructure mode requires that you specify the radio network your computer station is intended to connect to (the host station call sign), so set your computer station to recognize the SSID you assigned to the AP/wireless router to which you wish to connect.

You may need to use either an adaptor or a short pigtail to connect the card's MMCX antenna port or the interface's RP antenna connector to the N-series connector on the coaxial cable run to the antenna. Fortunately at the other end, most 2.4 GHz antennas come with a female N-series connector.

Team up with a nearby radio amateur to test. Do your initial testing in the same room together making sure the link-up is working. Then as you increase distances going toward your separate station locations, you can coordinate using a suitable local FM simplex frequency. You will increasingly need this communication to assist with directional antenna orientation as you get further apart.

Figure 7-7—The Linksys Wireless-G PCI Adapter WMP54G.

MOBILE HSMM OPERATING

When hams use the term "mobile HSMM station" what they are talking about is a wireless computer set-up in their vehicle to operate in a stationary portable fashion. Nobody is suggesting that you try to drive a vehicle and look at a computer screen at the same time! That would be very dangerous and possibly make you immediately eligible for the Silent Keys list in *QST* magazine! So unless you have someone else driving the vehicle, keep your eyes on the road and not on the computer screen!

What sort of equipment is needed to operate an HSMM mobile station?

■ A portable computer, such as laptop or mini-computer. A PDA might be made to work but software for such devices may be problematic. The operating system can be *Microsoft Windows*, *Linux*, or *Mac OS*, although *Microsoft XP* offers some better WLAN functionality.

■ PC Card wireless client adaptor card with at least one external antenna port.

■ Pig tail assembly as described earlier, with a short length of low-loss coaxial cable.

■ Topographic maps or mapping software of the area.

■ A small power inverter (~200W) to convert your vehicle's 13.8 Vdc to 115 Vac to keep the laptop battery charged. Running the laptop plus a small transceiver drains the onboard battery fairly quickly.

■ Two antennas. One omnidirectional magnet mount on the roof of the vehicle, and another directional antenna that can be clip mounted on a window edge or placed outside the vehicle on a small tripod or portable mast.

Some type of radio software hams call an *automatic monitor*, and computer buffs would call a *sniffer utility*. The most common type being used by hams is Marius Milner's *Network Stumbler for Windows* or *NetStumbler*. All operating systems have monitoring programs that are available. *Linux* has *Kismet*; *MAC OS* has *MacStumbler*. Marius Milner has a version for the PocketPC, which he calls *MiniStumbler*. Whichever monitoring utility you use, make certain it supports the specific PC card you are using too.

While operating your HSMM mobile station, if you monitor an unlicensed Part 15 station (non-ham), most types of WiFi equipment will automatically associate or link to such stations. Although Part 15 stations share the 2.4-GHz band on a non-interfering basis with hams, they are operating in another service. In another part of this section we will provide various steps you can take to prevent Part 15 stations from automatically linking with HSMM stations. So in like manner, except in the case of a communications emergency, we recommend that you do not use a Part 15 station's Internet connection for any radio amateur purpose.

HSMM AREA SURVEYS

Area or site surveys were mentioned earlier. Exactly how should these be conducted?

Both licensed amateurs (FCC Part 97 Regulations) and unlicensed (FCC Part 15 Regulations) stations use the 2.4-GHz band. To be a good neighbor, find out what others are doing in your area before designing your community HSMM radio network or long range link. This is easy to do using IEEE 802.11 modulation. Unless it has been disabled, an access point/router is constantly sending out an identification beacon known as its SSID. In HSMM practice this is simply the radio amateur station call sign (and perhaps the local radio club name) entered into the software configuration supplied on the CD that comes with the device.

An area or site survey using appropriate monitoring software, for example the free *NetStumbler* software downloaded and running on your PC (**www.netstumbler.com/index.php**), is recommended prior to starting up any HSMM operations. Slew your station's directional antenna through a 360-degree arc, and drive your HSMM mobile station (described earlier) around your local area. This HSMM area survey will identify and automatically log most other 802.11 station activity in your area. There are many different ways to avoid interference with other users of the band when planning your HSMM operations. Moving your operating frequency 2-3 channels away from the other stations is often sufficient.

RUNNING HIGH POWER

It is tempting for some radio amateurs to think that if they run higher power they will get better range out of their HSMM radio station. This is not always the case. There are many factors involved in range determination when operating UHF or microwave frequencies. The first and most significant of these is the lay of land (topology) and path obstructions. Running additional power is unlikely to correct for either of these impediments.

Second, running higher power to improve signal link margins often requires that this be done at both ends of the link to obtain meaningful results.

Third, most RF amplifiers for use with 802.11 modulations are of the BDA (bi-directional amplifier) type. They amplify both the incoming signal and the outgoing signal using a HS switch, with perhaps some AGC (automatic gain control) function in more sophisticated models. That means to get maximum effectiveness out of such devices they must be mounted as close as possible to the antenna.

Fourth, 802.11 signals from such inexpensive broadband devices often come with significant sidebands. This is not prime RF suitable for amplification! A tuned RF channel filter should be added to the system to reduce these sidebands and to avoid splatter.

Also, if your HSMM radio station is next door to an OSCAR satellite ground station or other licensed user of the band, you may need to take extra steps in order to avoid interfering with them, such as moving to channel 4 or even channel 5. In this case a tuned output filter may be necessary to avoid not only causing QRM, but also to prevent some of your now amplified sidebands from going outside the amateur band, which stops at 2450 MHz.

Nonetheless, achieving the network design objectives, especially in the case of EMCOM, may require the use of high-power to overcome the noise and Part 15 interference on the band. Higher power output may be needed to improve the reliability of the link. Generally when speaking of "high-power" HSMM radio amateurs mean 1-3 W of RF output power. Beyond that level becomes very expensive and the additional signal strength can be more economically and appropriately obtained with the use of higher gain, more directive antennas arrays.

Only after an HSMM radio link analysis (see **logidac.com/gfk/80211link/pathAnalysis.html**) clearly indicates that additional RF output power is required to achieve the desired path distance and a thorough RF area survey has been conducted, should more RF power output be considered. Even then, do not use higher power as a substitute for higher antenna gain at both ends of the link. Only after all reasonable efforts have been taken to get the highest possible antenna system gain and directivity, and the link is still not meeting requirements, should higher power be employed. At that point in the analysis showing that higher power is required, what is needed is called a *bi-directional amplifier*. It is usually mounted at the end of the antenna pig-tail near the top of the tower or mast for maximum efficiency. See **Figure 7-8**.

The importance of the RF area survey cannot be over emphasized. The control operator needs to be continually aware of the Part 15 surrounding activities and sources, especially along the directional path of the RF beamed signal from their station.

Figure 7-8—A typical bi-directional amplifier for HSMM applications. This unit delivers 1 W output.

To date radio amateurs have never been attributed to being the source of a library, school, police station's etc. WLAN being ground to a halt by being in the path of a strong Part 97 station signal running 1-3 W output. That may not sound like a lot of power, but it is much higher than normal Part 15 power. You don't want to be the first! Run higher power with care and only as a last resort. As radio amateurs we have the right, and the FCC has always supported that right against Part 15 objections, but the political reality is that Part 15 stations out number us by 100,000 to 1, if not more. Be careful, please!

Automatic Power Control

It should be noted that the existing FCC Amateur Radio regulations covering spread spectrum at the time this is be-

ing written were implemented prior to 802.11 being available. The provision in the existing regulations calling for automatic power control (APC) for RF power outputs in excess of 1 W is not considered technologically feasible in the case of 802.11 modulations for various reasons. As a result the FCC has communicated to the ARRL that the APC provision of the existing spread spectrum regulations are therefore not applicable to 802.11 emissions under Part 97.

However, using higher than normal output power in HSMM radio, in the shared 2.4 GHz band, is also something that should be done with considerable care, and only after careful analysis of link path conditions and the existing 802.11 activity in your area. Using the minimum power necessary for the communications is the law and has always been a good operating practice for hams.

HSMM ANTENNA SYSTEMS

There are a number of factors that determine the best antenna design for a specific HSMM radio application. Most commonly, HSMM stations use horizontal instead of vertical polarization. It seems to work better than vertical polarization. In addition, most Part 15 stations are vertically polarized, so this is sometimes thought to provide another small barrier between the two different services sharing the band. With multipath propagation is it doubtful how much real isolation this polarization change actually provides.

More importantly, most HSMM radio stations use highly directional antennas instead of omnidirectional antennas. Directional antennas provide significantly more gain and thus better signal-to-noise ratios, which in the case of 802.11 modulations means higher rate data throughput. Higher data throughput, in turn, translates into more multimedia radio capability. Look at **Figure 7-9**. The Valley ARA and the Massanutten ARA set up an elaborate HSMM network on Field Day, using high-gain directional antennas on mountaintops to span as much as 17 miles!

Highly directional antennas also have many other advantages. Such antennas can allow two radio amateurs to shoot their narrow beam width signals over, or shoot around, or even shoot between, other wireless stations on the band. However, the nature of 802.11 modulations coupled with the various configurations of many COTS devices allows hams to economically experiment with many other fascinating antenna designs. Such

unique antenna system designs can be used to simply help avoid interference, or to extend the range of the station. For example, much more experimenting needs to be done with the use of circularly polarized (CP) antennas instead of liner polarized

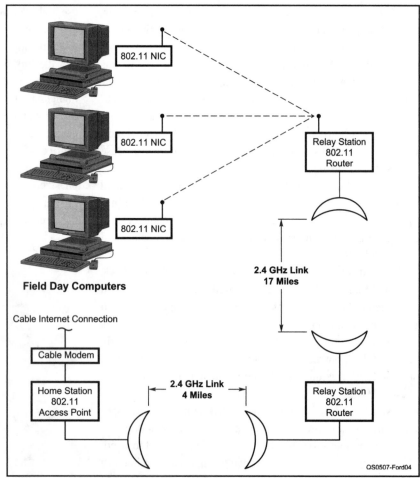

Field Day Computers

Figure 7-9—The Valley ARA and the Massanutten ARA set up this complex HSMM network for their Field Day operations. Note the long links supported by parabolic dish antennas, as well as the final link to the Internet.

antennas. What about the isolation provided between left-handed CP and right-handed CP? Would using two antennas of different handiness for receive space diversity produce significantly better reception? These are questions for which we don't have answers at this time.

Space Diversity

Some AP/wireless routers have space diversity capability built-into their design. However, as mentioned previously, it is not always operated in the same fashion, so check the literature or the Web site of your particular device manufacturer to be certain how the dual antenna ports are used. Many APs come equipped with two rubber ducky antennas and two antenna ports. One antenna port may be the primary and the other port the secondary input to the transceiver. Which signal input is used may depends on which antenna is providing the best S/N ratio at that specific instant.

The antenna spacing on the back panel of the AP provides a very minimum antenna separation to achieve space diversity. Try experimenting with two outside high-gain antennas spaced 10 or more wavelengths apart (that is only about one meter on the 2.4-GHz band). It may be very worthwhile in improving the quality of the link and the resulting speed of data throughput, especially on long links. Such extended radio paths tend to experience more multipath signal distortion. This multipath effect is caused by multiple signal reflections off various objects in the path of the linking signal. The use of space diversity techniques helps reduce this effect and thus improve the data rate throughput on the link. The higher the date rate means that more multimedia (MM) capability is built into radio link.

Circular Polarization

Another technique that warrants further investigation is the use of circular polarization. Radio amateurs have used such antennas for year in satellite communications. They are easily home-made devices. See **Figure 7-10**.

The use of circular polarization (CP) using helical antennas, patch feed-points on dish an-

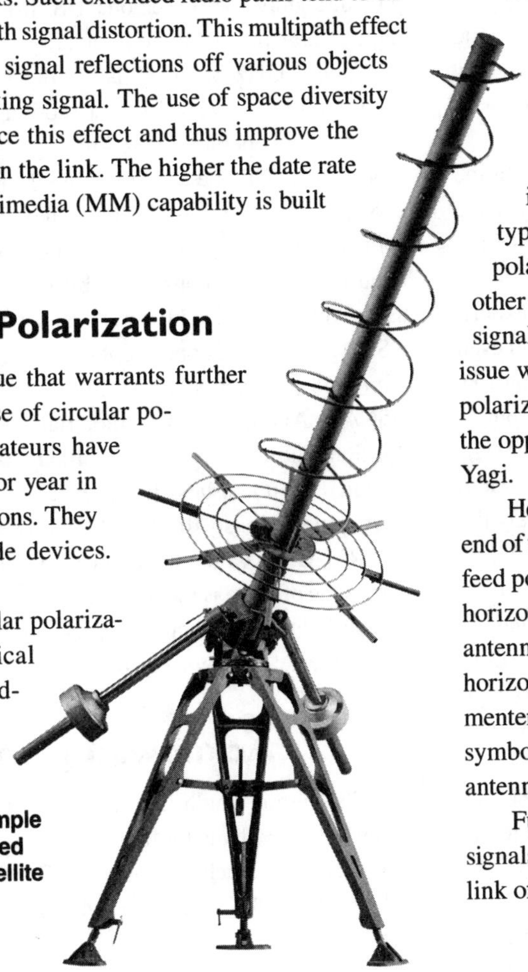

Figure 7-10—An example of a circularly polarized antenna used for satellite communications.

tennas or other means, warrants further study by radio amateurs. Remember this is HS digital radio. The use of CP antennas may help avoid symbol errors. Circularly polarized antennas should be used at both ends of the link. Also, be certain that the antennas are of the same *handedness*, for example, right-hand circular polarization (RHCP). The ability of circular polarization to enhance propagation of long-path HSMM radio signals should not be overlooked.

Circularly Polarized Space Diversity

A combination or hybrid antenna design combining both circularly polarized antennas and space diversity could yield some extraordinary signal propagation results. For example, it has been suggested that using an RHCP for one antenna and LHCP for the other antenna, plus using antenna spacing greater than 10 wavelengths, could provide a nearly "bullet-proof" design. Only actual field testing of such designs under different terrain features would reveal such potential.

Mixed Antenna Design Issue

In conventional wide-bandwidth analog radio antennas systems, so long as both antennas at both ends of a radio link have broad bandwidths and the same polarization, all is fine. While this may be true for wide bandwidth analog signals, such as amateur television VSB (vestigial sideband) signals or FM ATV signals, it may not be true for broad bandwidth high-speed digital signals.

802.11 signals produce very broadband signals, typically 20-22 MHz. There is evidence to date that indicates the use of a same polarized antenna with one type of feed point at one end of the link and the use of a same polarized antenna with a different type of feed point at the other end of the link, may introduce a problem with HS digital signals. A common example of this potential mixed-antenna issue would be if one HSMM radio station uses a horizontally polarized linear Yagi, while the other HSMM radio station at the opposite end of the link uses a horizontally polarized loop Yagi.

Here is another typical situation. Let us say the ham at one end of the radio path uses a dish antenna with a horizontal dipole feed point. The other ham at the opposite end of the path uses a horizontally polarized loop Yagi. Both antennas have gain, both antennas are broad bandwidth designs, and both antennas are horizontally polarized. Nonetheless, the radio amateur experimenters may experience higher BER (bit error rate) because of symbol errors caused by the different manner in which the two antennas manipulate the digital radio signal wave front.

Further radio amateur experimentation with HSMM radio signals is warranted to determine the full impact on the radio link of using mixed antenna types.

INFORMATION SECURITY

An HSMM radio station can be considered a form of software defined radio (SDR). Your computer running the appropriate software combined with the wireless adaptor or router creates a single unit, which is now your station's HSMM radio transceiver. Unlike other radios, your HSMM radio is now a networked radio device. It could be connected directly to other computers (ad hoc mode) and to other radio networks (infrastructure mode) and even to the Internet. So each HSMM radio station needs to be protected.

There are at least two basic steps that should be taken with regards to all HSMM radios:

(1) The PC should be provided with a current antivirus/anti-spyware program(s). This software must be regularly updated to remain effective. Such programs may have come with the PC when it was purchased. If that is not the case, reasonably priced and even free anti-virus programs are readily available from a number of sources, e.g. AVG (**http://free.grisoft.com/**).

(2) It is important to use a firewall software program or hardware on your HSMM radio. The firewall should be configured to allow all outgoing traffic, but to restrict all incoming traffic without specific authorization. Commercial personal computer firewall products are available from Symantec, ZoneLabs and McAfee Network Associates. Check this URL for a list of freeware firewalls for your personal computer: **www.webattack.com/freeware/security/fwfirewall.shtml**. Check this URL for a list of shareware firewalls for your personal computer: **www.webattack.com/Shareware/security/swfirewall.shtml**.

HSMM ON OTHER BANDS

Up to this point all the discussion has been regarding HSMM radio operations on the 2.4-GHz amateur band. However, 802.11 signals can be used on any amateur band above 902 MHz.

FM repeaters may not have a problem with sharing the frequency with 802.11 operations, since they would likely just hear an 802.11 modulated signal as weak background noise, and the 802.11 modulation, especially the OFDM channels used by 802.11g, would simply work around the FM interference with little negative impact.

There is some older 802.11 gear (FHSS) available on the surplus market for amateur experimentation. Alternatively, some form of frequency transverter may be used to take 2.4 GHz to the 902-MHz band.

The 1.2-GHz band has some potential for 802.11 experimenting. Some areas have several FM voice repeaters and even ATV FM repeaters on the band. But again these relatively narrow bandwidth signals would likely hear any 802.11 modulations as simply background noise.

Looking at the potential interference from the HSMM radio perspective, even in the case of the FM ATV, it is unlikely the signal would significantly disrupt the 802.11 modulation unless the two signals were on exactly the same center frequency or at least with complete overlap in bandwidth. Keep in mind that the FM ATV signal is only several megahertz wide, but the 802.11 modulation is 20 - 22 MHz wide. For the analog signal to wipe out the spread spectrum signal, it would need to overpower or completely swamp the 802.11 receiver's front end.

The 3.5-GHz band offers some real possibilities for 802.11 developments. Frequency transverters are available to get to the band from 2.4 GHz and there is little other activity on the band at this time. Developments in Europe of 802.16 with 108 Mbit/s data throughput may make 3.5-GHz gear available for amateur experimentation in the US. Radio amateurs are investigating the feasibility of using such gear when it becomes available in the US for providing a RMAN or *radio metropolitan area networks*. The RMAN would be used to link the individual HSMM radio repeaters (AP/wireless routers) or RLANs together in order to provide county-wide or regional HSMM radio coverage, depending on the Amateur Radio population density.

The 5-GHz band is also being investigated. Some US manufactured COTS 802.11a modulation gear has OFDM channels that operate in this Amateur Radio band. The 802.11a modulation could be used in a HSMM RLAN operating much as 802.11g is in the 2.4-GHz band. It is also being considered by some HSMM groups as a means of providing MAN links. This band is also being considered by AMSAT for what is known as an ADX (Advanced Digital Transponder). This would be an HSMM radio transponder onboard a Phase-3 high orbit satellite (HOS), or even a high-altitude or a Phase-4 geostationary OSCAR. Another form of modulation such as TDMA (time division multiple access) would likely have to be used because of signal timing issues and other factors, but the concept is at least being seriously discussed.

RMAN link alternatives are also being tested by radio amateurs. One of these is the use of *virtual private networks* (VPN) similar to the method currently used to provide worldwide FM voice repeater links via the Internet.

Acknowledgements

The author would like to express his appreciation to the following individuals for their intellectual contributions to this chapter: Nathan Duehr, WYØX; Tim Gorman, ABØWR, Douglas Kilgore, KD5OUG and Les Rayburn, N1LF.

APPENDIX A

AX.25 Link Access Protocol
for Amateur Packet Radio

Version 2.2
Revision: July 1998

Copyright (c) 1997 by Tucson Amateur Packet Radio Con
Portions Copyright (c) 1984, 1993 by The American Rad

Authors:
 William A. Beech, NJ7P
 Douglas E. Nielsen, N7LEM
 Jack Taylor, N7OO

Edited by:
 Lee Knoper, N7CUU
 73223.262@compuserve.com

Production Editors:
 Greg Jones, WD5IVD, wd5ivd@tapr.org

1. Abstract

This document details AX.25 version 2.2 digital communication standard. The objective of this standard is to ensure link-layer compatibility between stations. This document is intended to assist the designers and users of amateur packet radio equipment by providing a high-level common reference publication. However, the existence of this protocol is not intended to disparage anyone from designing, marketing or using products, processes or procedures not conforming to the protocol.

As with any evolving technical standard, this protocol is subject to periodic review. Interested parties are encouraged to use the latest edition.

1.1. General

The amateur radio community has expressed the need and desire to define a protocol that can accept and reliably deliver data over a variety of communications links between two signaling terminals. The AX.25 version 2.2 Link-Layer Protocol provides this service, independent of the existence of any upper layer.

This protocol conforms to International Standards Organization (ISO) Information Standards (IS) 3309, 4335 and 7809 High-level Data Link Control (HDLC) and uses terminology found in these documents. It also follows the principles of Consultative Committee in International Telegraph and Telephone (CCITT) Recommendation Q.920 and Q.921 (LAP-D) in the use of multiple links, distinguished by the address field, on a single shared channel. Parameter negotiation was extracted from ISO IS 8885. The data-link service definitions were extracted from ISO IS 8886.

As defined, this protocol works equally well in either half- or full-duplex amateur radio environments, and has been improved for operation over partially impaired HF circuits.

It works equally well for direct connections between two individual amateur packet radio stations, or between an individual station and a multi-port controller.

It permits the establishment of more than one link-layer connection per device, if the device is so capable.

It also permits self-connections. A self-connection occurs when a device establishes a link to itself using its own address for both the source and destination of the frame.

Most link-layer protocols assume that one primary (or master) device (generally called a Data Circuit Terminating Equipment, or DCE), is connected to one or more secondary (or slave) device(s) (usually called a Data Terminating Equipment, or DTE). This type of unbalanced operation is not practical in a shared RF amateur radio environment. Instead, AX.25 assumes that both ends of the link are of the same class, thereby eliminating the two different classes of devices.

In this protocol specification, the phrase Terminal Node Controller (TNC) refers to the balanced type of device found in amateur packet radio. Other standards refer to these peer entities as DXEs.

2. Concepts and Terminology

2.1. Basic Concepts

ISO has developed a reference model for Open Systems Interconnection (OSI) to better facilitate the interconnection of different types of computing systems. The basic structuring technique in this reference model is known as layering. According to this technique, communication among application processes is viewed as being logically partitioned into an ordered set of layers represented in a vertical sequence as shown in Figure 2.1. Each layer provides a Service Access Point (SAP) for interface to the next higher layer. Note that any layer may be a null, where no function or code is provided. Such is the case with the current TAPR TNC-2 equipment, where only Layers 1, 2 and 7 are provided; these comprise the minimum configuration for reliable communications.

Layer	Function
7	Application
6	Presentation
5	Session
4	Transport
3	Network
2	Data Link
1	Physical

Figure 2.1. Seven layer OSI reference model.

2.2. AX.25 Model

The two lower layers, data link and physical, can be further subdivided into several distinct finite state machines as shown in Figure 2.2. This example shows a single link to the radio port.

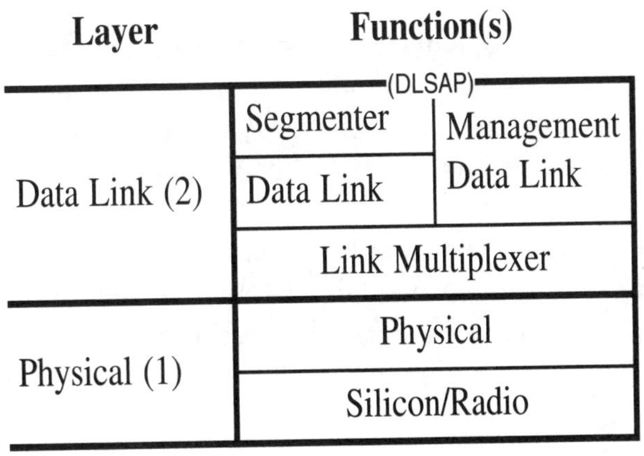

Layer	Function(s)	
	——————(DLSAP)——————	
Data Link (2)	Segmenter	Management
	Data Link	Data Link
	Link Multiplexer	
Physical (1)	Physical	
	Silicon/Radio	

Figure 2.2. AX.25 finite state machine model (single link).

Figure 2.3 shows an example of multiple links to the radio port. The link multiplexer described in this standard multiplexes multiple data-link connections into one physical connection. A separate data-link machine must be provided for each connection allowed by the implementation.

Layer   **Function(s)**

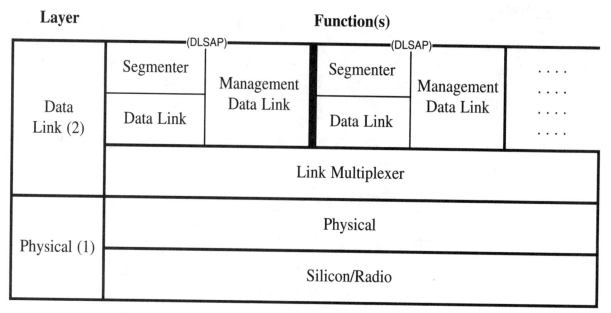

Figure 2.3. AX.25 finite state machine model (multiple stream).

2.3. Data-Link Service Access Point

Figures 2.2 and 2.3 indicate a Data-Link Service Access Point (DLSAP) at the upper boundary of Layer 2. This DLSAP is the point at which the data-link layer provides services to Layer 3. Associated with each DLSAP is one or more data-link connection endpoint(s).

Entities exist in each layer. Entities may be the Link Multiplexer, Data Link, Management Data Link or Segmenter. Entities in the same layer, but in different systems that must exchange information to achieve a common objective, are called "peer entities." Entities in adjacent layers interact through their common boundary. The services provided by the data-link layer are the combination of the services and functions provided by both the data-link layer and the physical layer.

Cooperation between data-link layer entities is governed by a peer-to-peer protocol specific to the layer. For example, when information is to be exchanged between two Layer 3 entities, an association must be established between the entities through the data-link layer using the AX.25 protocol. This association is called a data-link connection. Data-link connections are provided by the data-link layer between two or more DLSAPs.

Layer 3 requests services from the data-link layer via command/response interactions known as service "primitives." (Similarly, the interaction between the data-link layer and the physical layer also occurs via service primitives.) Primitives are discussed in greater detail in Section 5.

The primitives that are exchanged between the data-link layer and adjacent layers are of the following four types:

a) REQUEST primitive type: used by a higher layer to request a service from the next lower layer;

b) INDICATION primitive type: used by a layer to provide a service to notify the next higher layer of any specific activity that is service related. The INDICATION primitive may be the result of an activity of the lower layer related to the primitive type REQUEST at the peer entity;

c) RESPONSE primitive type: used by a layer to acknowledge receipt from a lower layer of the primitive type INDICATION. AX.25 does not use the RESPONSE primitive; and

d) CONFIRM primitive type: used by a layer to provide the requested service to confirm that the activity has been completed.

Figure 2.4 illustrates the use of the four primitive types in conjunction with the connect primitive.

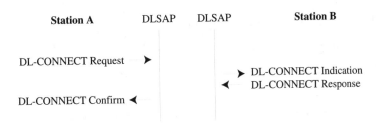

Figure 2.4. Example use of primitive types.

2.4. Segmenter

The Segmenter State Machine accepts input from the higher layer through the DLSAP. If the unit of data to be sent exceeds the limits of a AX.25 Information (I) frame (see Section 4.3.1) or Unnumbered Information (UI) frame (see Section 4.3.3.6), the segmenter breaks the unit down into smaller segments for transmission. Incoming segments are reassembled for delivery to the higher layer and passed through the DLSAP. The segmenter passes all other signals unchanged.

One segmenter exists per data link. Because a single piece of equipment may have multiple data links in operation simultaneously (e.g., to support multiple higher-layer applications), there can be multiple, independently operating segmenters within the equipment.

2.5. Data Link

The Data-link State Machine is the heart of the AX.25 protocol. The Data-link State Machine provides all logic necessary to establish and release connections between two stations and to exchange information in a connectionless (i.e., via UI frames) and connection-oriented (i.e., via I frames with recovery procedures) manner.

One Data-link State Machine exists per data link. Because a single piece of equipment may have multiple data links in operation simultaneously (e.g., to support multiple higher layer applications), there can be multiple, independently operating data-link machines within the equipment.

2.6. Management Data Link

The Management Data-link State Machine provides for the parameter negotiation of the AX.25 protocol. The Management Data-link State Machine provides all logic necessary to negotiate operating parameters between two stations.

One Management Data-link State Machine exists per data link. Because a single piece of equipment may have multiple data links in operation simultaneously (e.g., to support multiple higher layer applications), there can be multiple, independently operating management data-link machines within the equipment.

2.7. Link Multiplexer

The Link Multiplexer State Machine allows one or more data links to share the same physical (radio) channel. The Link Multiplexer State Machine provides the logic necessary to give each data link an opportunity to use the channel, according to the rotation algorithm embedded within the link multiplexer.

One Link Multiplexer State Machine exists per physical channel. If a single piece of equipment has multiple physical channels operating simultaneously, then an independently operating Link Multiplexer State Machine exists for each channel.

2.8. Physical

The Physical State Machine manipulates the radio transmitter and receiver. One Physical State Machine exists per physical channel.

Because different types of radio channel operations are used, the Physical State Machine exists in different forms. Each form hides the peculiar characteristics of each radio channel from the higher layer state machines. Two Physical State Machines have been defined in this standard: simplex and full duplex Physical State Machines.

3. Frame Structure

Link layer packet radio transmissions are sent in small blocks of data, called frames.

There are three general types of AX.25 frames:
- a) Information frame (I frame);
- b) Supervisory frame (S frame); and
- c) Unnumbered frame (U frame).

Each frame is made up of several smaller groups, called fields. Figures 3.1a and 3.1b illustrate the three basic types of frames. Note that the first bit to be transmitted is on the left side.

Flag	Address	Control	Info	FCS	Flag
01111110	112/224 Bits	8/16 Bits	N*8 Bits	16 Bits	01111110

Figure 3.1a. U and S frame construction.

Flag	Address	Control	PID	Info	FCS	Flag
01111110	112/224 Bits	8/16 Bits	8 Bits	N*8 Bits	16 Bits	01111110

Figure 3.1b. Information frame construction.

Notes:
- The Info field exists only in certain frames (Section 4.4.3)
- FCS is the Frame Check Sequence field (Section 4.4.6)
- PID is the Protocol Identifier field (Section 3.4)

Each field is made up of an integral number of octets (8-bit byte of binary data) and serves the specific function outlined below.

All fields except the Frame Check Sequence (FCS) are transmitted low-order bit first. FCS is transmitted bit 15 first.

3.1. Flag Field

The flag field is one octet long. Because the flag delimits frames, it occurs at both the beginning and end of each frame. Two frames may share one flag, which would denote the end of the first frame and the start of the next frame. A flag consists of a zero followed by six ones followed by another zero, or 01111110 (7E hex). As a result of bit stuffing (see Section 3.6), this sequence is not allowed to occur anywhere else inside a complete frame.

3.2. Address Field

The address field identifies both the source of the frame and its destination. In addition, the address field contains the command/response information and facilities for Layer 2 repeater operation.

The encoding of the address field is described in Section 3.12.

3.3. Control Field

The control field identifies the type of frame being passed and controls several attributes of the Layer 2 connection. It is one or two octets in length; its encoding is discussed in Section 4.2.

3.4. PID Field

The Protocol Identifier (PID) field appears in information frames (I and UI) only. It identifies which kind of Layer 3 protocol, if any, is in use.

The PID itself is not included as part of the octet count of the information field. The encoding of the PID is as follows:

HEX	M S B L S B	Translation
**	yy01yyyy	AX.25 layer 3 implemented.
**	yy10yyyy	AX.25 layer 3 implemented.
0x01	00000001	ISO 8208/CCITT X.25 PLP
0x06	00000110	Compressed TCP/IP packet. Van Jacobson (RFC 1144)
0x07	00000111	Uncompressed TCP/IP packet. Van Jacobson (RFC 1144)
0x08	00001000	Segmentation fragment
0xC3	11000011	TEXNET datagram protocol
0xC4	11000100	Link Quality Protocol
0xCA	11001010	Appletalk
0xCB	11001011	Appletalk ARP
0xCC	11001100	ARPA Internet Protocol
0xCD	11001101	ARPA Address resolution
0xCE	11001110	FlexNet
0xCF	11001111	NET/ROM
0xF0	11110000	No layer 3 protocol implemented.
0xFF	11111111	Escape character. Next octet contains more Level 3 protocol information.
Escape character. Next octet contains more Level 3 protocol information.	00001000	

Figure 3.2. PID definitions.

Where:

An "Y" indicates all combinations used.

Note: All forms of YY11YYYY and YY00YYYY other than those listed above are reserved at this time for future Layer 3 protocols. The assignment of these formats is subject to mutual agreement among amateur radio operators. It is recommended that the creators of Layer 3 protocols contact the ARRL for suggested encodings.

3.5. Information Field
The information (I) field conveys user data from one end of the link to the other.

The I fields are allowed in only five types of frames:

a) The I frame;
b) The UI frame;
c) The XID frame;
d) The TEST frame; and
e) The FRMR frame.

The I field defaults to a length of 256 octets and contains an integral number of octets. These constraints apply prior to the insertion of zero bits as specified in Section 3.6. Any information in the I field is passed along the link transparently, except for the zero-bit insertion (see Section 3.6) necessary to prevent flags from accidentally appearing in the I field.

3.6. Bit Stuffing
In order to ensure that the flag bit sequence mentioned above does not appear accidentally anywhere else in a frame, the sending station monitors the bit sequence for a group of five or more contiguous "1" bits. Any time five contiguous "1" bits are sent, the sending station inserts a "0" bit after the fifth "1" bit. During frame reception, any time five contiguous "1" bits are received, a "0" bit immediately following five "1" bits is discarded.

3.7. Frame-Check Sequence
The Frame-Check Sequence (FCS) is a sixteen-bit number calculated by both the sender and the receiver of a frame. It ensures that the frame was not corrupted by the transmission medium. The Frame-Check Sequence is calculated in accordance with recommendations in the HDLC reference document, ISO 3309.

3.8. Order of Bit Transmission
The FCS field of an AX.25 frame is sent most-significant bit first. All other fields are sent with each octet's least-significant bit first.

3.9. Invalid Frames
A frame is considered by the link layer to be an invalid frame if it:

a) consists of less than 136 bits (including the opening and closing flags);
b) is not bounded by opening and closing flags; or
c) is not octet aligned (an integral number of octets).

3.10. Frame Abort

If a frame must be prematurely aborted, at least fifteen contiguous "1"s are sent without bit stuffing added.

3.11. Inter-Frame Time Fill

Whenever it is necessary for a TNC to keep its transmitter on while not actually sending frames, the time between frames should be filled with contiguous flags.

3.12. Address-Field Encoding

The address field of all frames consists of a destination, source and (optionally) two Layer 2 repeater subfields. Each subfield consists of an amateur callsign and a Secondary Station Identifier (SSID). The callsign is made up of upper-case alpha and numeric ASCII characters only. The SSID is a four-bit integer that uniquely identifies multiple stations using the same amateur callsign.

The HDLC address field is extended beyond one octet by assigning the least-significant bit of each octet to be an "extension bit." The extension bit of each octet is set to "0" to indicate the next octet contains more address information, or to "1", to indicate that this is the last octet of the HDLC address field. To make room for this extension bit, the amateur radio call-sign information is shifted one bit left.

3.12.1. Non-repeater Address-Field Encoding

If Layer 2 repeaters are not being used, the address field is encoded as shown in Figure 3.3. The destination address is the callsign and SSID of the amateur radio station to which the frame is addressed. The source address contains the amateur callsign and SSID of the station that sent the frame. These callsigns are the callsigns of the two ends of a Layer 2 AX.25 link only.

First
Octet
Sent

Address Field of Frame	
Destination Address Subfield	Source Address Subfield
A1 A2 A3 A4 A5 A6 A7	A8 A9 A10 A11 A12 A13 A14

Figure 3.3. Non-repeater address-field encoding.

A1 through A14, above, are the fourteen octets that make up the two address subfields of the address field. The destination subfield is seven octets long (A1 through A7), and is sent first. This address sequence provides the receivers of frames time to check the destination address subfield to see if the frame is addressed to them while the rest of the frame is being received. The source address subfield is then sent in octets A8 through A14. Both of these subfields are encoded in the same manner, except that the last octet of the address field has the HDLC address extension bit set.

The SSID octet at the end of each address subfield (A7 and A14) contains the SSID and the "C" bit. The C bits identify command and response frames (see Section 6.1.2). The SSID octet at the end of each optional Layer 2 repeater address subfield (A21 and A28) contains the SSID and the "H" bit ("[H]as-been-repeated"). The H bits indicate that the Layer 2 repeater station has repeated the frame (see Section 3.12.3). Each SSID octet contains two bits that are reserved for future use.

Figure 3.4 shows a typical AX.25 frame in the non-repeater mode of operation.

Octet	ASCII	Bin Data	Hex Data
Flag		01111110	7E
A1	N	10011000	98
A2	J	10010100	94
A3	7	01101110	6E
A4	P	10100000	A0
A5	space	01000000	40
A6	space	01000000	40
A7	SSID	11100000	E0
A8	N	10011000	98
A9	7	01101110	6E
A10	L	10011000	98
A11	E	10001010	8A
A12	M	10011010	9A
A13	space	01000000	40
A14	SSID	01100001	61
Control	I	00111110	3E
PID	none	11110000	F0
FCS	part1	XXXXXXXX	HH
FCS	part2	XXXXXXXX	HH
Flag		01111110	7E

Bit position   76543210

Figure 3.4. Non-repeater AX.25 frame.

The frame shown is an I frame, not going through a Layer 2 repeater, from N7LEM (SSID=0) to NJ7P (SSID=0), without a Layer 3 protocol. The P/F bit is set; the receive sequence number [N(R)] is 1; the send sequence number [N(S)] is 7.

3.12.2. Destination Subfield Encoding

Figure 3.5 shows how an amateur callsign is placed in the destination address subfield, occupying octets A1 through A7.

Octet	ASCII	Bin Data	Hex Data
A1	N	10011000	98
A2	J	10010100	94
A3	7	01101110	6E
A4	P	10100000	A0
A5	space	01000000	40
A6	space	01000000	40
A7	SSID	11100000	E0
A7	SSID	CRRSSID0	

Bit position   76543210

Figure 3.5. Destination field encoding.

Where:

a) The top octet (A1) is the first octet sent, with bit 0 of each octet being the first bit sent, and bit 7 being the last bit sent.

b) The first (low-order or bit 0) bit of each octet is the HDLC address extension bit, set to zero on all but the last octet in the address field, where it is set to one.

c) The bits marked "R" are reserved bits. They may be used in an agreed-upon manner in individual networks. When not implemented, they are set to one.

d) The bit marked "C" is the command/response bit of an AX.25 frame, as outlined in Section 6.1.2.

e) The characters of the callsign are standard seven-bit ASCII (upper case only) placed in the left-most seven bits of the octet to make room for the address extension bit. If the callsign contains fewer than six characters, it is padded with ASCII spaces between the last call sign character and the SSID octet.

f) The 0000 SSID is reserved for the first personal AX.25 station. This provision establishes one standard SSID for "normal" stations to use for the first station.

3.12.3. Source Subfield Encoding

Figure 3.6 shows how an amateur callsign is placed in the destination address subfield, occupying octets A1 through A7.

Octet	ASCII	Bin Data	Hex Data
A8	N	10011000	98
A9	7	01101110	6E
A10	L	10011000	98
A11	E	10001010	8A
A12	M	10011010	9A
A13	space	01000000	40
A14	SSID	CRRSSID0	

Bit position   76543210

Figure 3.6. Source field encoding.

Where:

a) The top octet (A8) is the first octet sent, with bit 0 of each octet being the first bit sent, and bit 7 being the last bit sent.

b) The first (low-order or bit 0) bit of each octet is the HDLC address extension bit, set to zero on all but the last octet in the address field, where it is set to one.

c) The bits marked "R" are reserved bits. They may be used in an agreed-upon manner in individual networks. When not implemented, they are set to one.

d) The bit marked "C" is the command/response bit of an LA PA frame, as outlined in Section 6.1.2.

e) The characters of the callsign are standard seven-bit ASCII (upper case only) placed in the leftmost seven bits of the octet to make room for the address extension bit. If the callsign contains fewer than six characters, it is padded with ASCII spaces between the last callsign character and the SSID octet.

f) The 0000 SSID is reserved for the first personal AX.25 station. This provision establishes one standard SSID for "normal" stations to use for the first station.

3.12.4. Layer 2 Repeater Address Encoding

Evolving consensus opinion is that repeater chaining belongs to a higher protocol layer. Consequently, it is being phased out of Layer 2, although backward compatibility is being maintained with a limit of two repeaters.

If a frame is to go through Layer 2 amateur packet repeater(s), an additional address subfield is appended to the end of the address field. This additional subfield contains the callsign(s) of the repeater(s) to be used. This allows more than one repeater to share the same RF channel. If this subfield exists, the last octet of the source subfield has its address extension bit set to "0", indicating that more address-field data follows. The repeater address subfield is encoded in the same manner as the destination and source address subfields, except for the most-significant bit in the last octet, called the H bit. As discussed in Section 3.12.1, the H bit indicates whether a frame has been repeated or not.

The H bit is set to "0" on frames going to a repeater. The repeater changes the H bit to "1" before it retransmits the frame. Stations monitor and repeat frames that meet the following conditions:

a) the frame is addressed to this station in a repeater address subfield;
b) the H bit in its repeater address subfield is 0; or
c) all previous H bits are set to one.

Figure 3.7 shows how the repeater address subfield is encoded. Figure 3.8 is an example of a complete frame after being repeated.

Octet	ASCII	Bin Data	Hex Data
A15	N	10011000	98
A16	J	10010100	94
A17	7	01101110	6E
A18	P	10100000	A0
A19	space	01000000	40
A20	space	01000000	40
A21	SSID	HRRSSID1	

Bit position   76543210

Figure 3.7. Repeater address encoding.

Where:

a) The top octet is the first octet sent, with bit 0 being sent first and bit 7 sent last of each octet.

b) As with the source and destination address subfields discussed above, bit 0 of each octet is the HDLC address extension bit, is set to "0" on all but the last address octet, where it is set to "1".

c) The "R" bits are reserved in the same manner as in the source and destination subfields.

d) The "H" bit is the has-been-repeated bit. It is set to "0" when a frame has not been repeated, and set to "1" by the repeating station when repeated.

Octet	ASCII	Bin Data	Hex Data
Flag		01111110	7E
A1	N	10011000	98
A2	J	10010100	94
A3	7	01101110	6E
A4	P	10100000	A0
A5	space	01000000	40
A6	space	01000000	40
A7	SSID	11100000	E0
A8	N	10011000	98
A9	7	01101110	6E
A10	L	10011000	98
A11	E	10001010	8A
A12	M	10011010	9A
A13	space	01000000	40
A14	SSID	01100000	60
A15	N	10011000	98
A16	7	01101110	6E
A17	O	10011110	9E
A18	O	10011110	9E
A19	space	01000000	40
A20	space	01000000	40
A21	SSID	11100011	E3
Control	I	00111110	3E
PID	none	11110000	F0
FCS	part 1	XXXXXXXX	HH
FCS	part 2	XXXXXXXX	HH
Flag		01111110	7E

Bit position   76543210

Figure 3.8. AX.25 frame in repeater mode.

The above frame is the same as shown in Figure 3.3, except for the addition of a repeater address subfield (N7OO, SSID=1). The H bit is set, indicating this frame is from the output of the repeater.

3.12.5. Multiple Repeater Operation

The link-layer AX.25 protocol allows operation through more than one repeater. Up to two repeaters may be used by extending the repeater address subfield. When there is more than one repeater address, the repeater address immediately following the source address subfield will be considered the address of the first repeater of a multiple-repeater chain. As a frame progresses through a chain of repeaters, each successive repeater will set the H bit in its SSID octet, indicating that the frame has been successfully repeated through it. No other changes to the frame are made (except for the necessary recalculation of the FCS). The destination station can determine the route the frame took to reach it by examining the address field and use this path to return frames.

The number of repeater addresses is variable. The last repeater address will have the address extension bit of the SSID octet set to "1" indicating the end of the address field. All other address octets will have their address extension bit set to "0".

Note that various timers (see Section 6.6.1) may require adjustment to accommodate the additional delays encountered when a frame must pass through a multiple-repeater chain.

4. Elements of Procedure and Formats of Fields

4.1. General

The elements of procedure define the command and response frames used on the AX.25 link.

Procedures are built from these elements and are described in Section 6.

4.2. Control Fields

The control field identifies the type of frame being sent. The control fields in AX.25 are modeled after the ISO HDLC balanced operation control fields.

4.2.1. Control-Field Formats

The three formats of control fields used in AX.25 are the:

a) Information frame (I frame);

b) Supervisory frame (S frame); and

c) Unnumbered frame (U frame).

Figures 4.1a and 4.1b illustrate the basic format of the control field associated with each of these three types of frames.

The control field can be one or two octets long and may use sequence numbers to maintain link integrity. These sequence numbers may be three-bit (modulo 8) or seven-bit (modulo 128) integers.

Control Field Type	Control-Field Bits			
	7 6 5	4	3 2 1 0	
I Frame	N(R)	P	N(S)	0
S Frame	N(R)	P/F	S S 0 1	
U Frame	M M M	P/F	M M 1 1	

Figure 4.1a. Control-field formats (modulo 8).

Control Field Type	Control-Field Bits			
	15 14 13 12 11 10 9	8	7 6 5 4 3 2 1 0	
I Frame	N(R)	P	N(S)	0
S Frame	N(R)	P/F	0 0 0 S S 0	1

Figure 4.1b. Control-field formats (modulo 128).

Where:

a) Bit 0 is the first bit sent and bit 7 (or bit 15 for modulo 128) is the last bit sent of the control field.

b) N(S) is the send sequence number (bit 1 is the LSB).

c) N(R) is the receive sequence number [bit 5 (or bit 9 for modulo 128) is the LSB].

d) The "S" bits are the supervisory function bits; their encoding is discussed in Section 4.2.1.2.

e) The "M" bits are the unnumbered frame modifier bits; their encoding is discussed in Section 4.2.1.3.

f) The P/F bit is the Poll/Final bit. The P/F bit is used in all types of frames. The P/F bit is also used in a command (poll) mode to request an immediate reply to a frame. The reply to this poll is indicated by setting the response (final) bit in the appropriate frame. Only one outstanding poll condition per direction is allowed at a time. The procedure for P/F bit operation is described in Section 6.2.

4.2.1.1. Information-Transfer Format
All I frames have bit 0 of the control field set to "0". N(S) is the sender's send sequence number (the send sequence number of this frame). N(R) is the sender's receive sequence number (the sequence number of the next expected receive frame). These numbers are described in Section 4.2.4.

4.2.1.2. Supervisory Format
Supervisory frames have bit 0 of the control field set to "1", and bit 1 of the control field set to "0". S frames provide supervisory link control such as acknowledging or requesting retransmission of I frames, and link-layer window control. Because S frames do not have an information field, the sender's send variable and the receiver's receive variable are not incremented for S frames.

4.2.1.3. Unnumbered Format
Unnumbered frames have both bits 0 and 1 of the control field set to "1". U frames are responsible for maintaining additional control over the link beyond what is accomplished with S frames. U frames are responsible for establishing and terminating link connections. U frames also allow for the transmission and reception of information outside of the normal flow control. Some U frames may contain both information and PID fields.

4.2.2. Control-Field Parameters

4.2.3. Sequence Numbers

If modulo 8 operation is in effect (the default), an I frame is assigned a sequential number from 0 to 7. This step allows up to seven outstanding I frames per Layer 2 connection at one time.

If modulo 128 operation is in effect, an I frame is assigned a sequential number between 0 and 127. This step allows up to 127 outstanding I frames per Layer 2 connection at one time.

4.2.4. Frame Variables and Sequence Numbers

4.2.4.1. Send State Variable V(S)

The send state variable exists within the TNC and is never sent. It contains the next sequential number to be assigned to the next transmitted I frame. This variable is updated with the transmission of each I frame.

4.2.4.2. Send Sequence Number N(S)

The send sequence number is found in the control field of all I frames. It contains the sequence number of the I frame being sent. Just prior to the transmission of the I frame, N(S) is updated to equal the send state variable.

4.2.4.3. Receive State Variable V(R)

The receive state variable exists within the TNC. It contains the sequence number of the next expected received I frame. This variable is updated upon the reception of an error-free I frame whose send sequence number equals the present received state variable value.

4.2.4.4. Received Sequence Number N(R)

The received sequence number exists in both I and S frames. Prior to sending an I or S frame, this variable is updated to equal that of the received state variable, thus implicitly acknowledging the proper reception of all frames up to and including N(R)-1.

4.2.4.5. Acknowledge State Variable V(A)

The acknowledge state variable exists within the TNC and is never sent. It contains the sequence number of the last frame acknowledged by its peer [V(A)-1 equals the N(S) of the last acknowledged I frame].

4.3. Control-Field Coding for Commands and Responses

4.3.1. Information Command Frame Control Field

The information (I) command transfers sequentially-numbered frames containing an information field across a data link.

The information-frame control field is encoded as shown in Figures 4.2a and 4.2b. These frames are sequentially numbered by the N(S) subfield to maintain control of their passage over the link-layer connection.

Control Field Type	Control-Field Bits			
	7 6 5	4	3 2 1	0
Information	N(R)	P	N(S)	0

Figure 4.2a. I frame control field (modulo 8).

Control Field Type	Control-Field Bits			
	Second Octet		First Octet	
	15 14 13 12 11 10 9	8	7 6 5 4 3 2 1	0
I Frame	N(R)	P	N(S)	0

Figure 4.2b. I frame control field (modulo 128).

4.3.2. Supervisory Frame Control Field

The supervisory frame control fields are encoded as shown in Figures 4.3a and 4.3b.

Control Field Type		Control-Field Bits			
		7 6 5	4	3 2	1 0
Receive Ready	RR	N(R)	P/F	0 0	0 1
Receive Not Ready	RNR	N(R)	P/F	0 1	0 1
Reject	REJ	N(R)	P/F	1 0	0 1
Selective Reject	SREJ	N(R)	P/F	1 1	0 1

Figure 4.3a. S frame control fields (modulo 8).

Control Field Type	Control-Field Bits			
	Second Octet		First Octet	
	15 14 13 12 11 10 9	8	7 6 5 4 3 2 1 0	
RR	N(R)	P/F	0 0 0 0 0 0 0 1	
RNR	N(R)	P/F	0 0 0 0 0 1 0 1	
REJ	N(R)	P/F	0 0 0 0 1 0 0 1	
SREJ	N(R)	P/F	0 0 0 0 1 1 0 1	

Figure 4.3b. S frame control fields (modulo 128).

Where:

Acronym	Description of Frame Identifiers
RR	Receive Ready - System Ready To Receive.
RNR	Receive Not Ready - TNC Buffer Full.
REJ	Reject Frame - Out of Sequence or Duplicate.
SREJ	Selective Reject - Request single frame repeat.

4.3.2.1. Receive Ready (RR) Command and Response

Receive Ready accomplishes the following:

a) indicates that the sender of the RR is now able to receive more I frames;
b) acknowledges properly received I frames up to, and including N(R)-1;and
c) clears a previously-set busy condition created by an RNR command having been sent.

The status of the TNC at the other end of the link can be requested by sending an RR command frame with the P-bit set to one.

4.3.2.2. Receive Not Ready (RNR) Command and Response

Receive Not Ready indicates to the sender of I frames that the receiving TNC is temporarily busy and cannot accept any more I frames. Frames up to N(R)-1 are acknowledged. Frames N(R) and above that may have been transmitted are discarded and must be retransmitted when the busy condition clears.

The RNR condition is cleared by the sending of a UA, RR, REJ or SABM(E) frame.

The status of the TNC at the other end of the link is requested by sending an RNR command frame with the P bit set to one.

4.3.2.3. Reject (REJ) Command and Response

The reject frame requests retransmission of I frames starting with N(R). Any frames sent with a sequence number of N(R)-1 or less are acknowledged. Additional I frames which may exist may be appended to the retransmission of the N(R) frame.

Only one reject frame condition is allowed in each direction at a time. The reject condition is cleared by the proper reception of I frames up to the I frame that caused the reject condition to be initiated.

The status of the TNC at the other end of the link is requested by sending a REJ command frame with the P bit set to one.

4.3.2.4. Selective Reject (SREJ) Command and Response

The selective reject, SREJ, frame is used by the receiving TNC to request retransmission of the single I frame numbered N(R). If the P/F bit in the SREJ frame is set to "1", then I frames numbered up to N(R)-1 inclusive are considered as acknowledged. However, if the P/F bit in the SREJ frame is set to "0", then the N(R) of the SREJ frame does not indicate acknowledgement of I frames.

Each SREJ exception condition is cleared (reset) upon receipt of the I frame with an N(S) equal to the N(R) of the SREJ frame.

A receiving TNC may transmit one or more SREJ frames, each containing a different N(R) with the P bit set to "0", before one or more earlier SREJ exception conditions have been cleared. However, a SREJ is not transmitted if an earlier REJ exception condition has not been cleared as indicated in Section 4.5.4. (To do so would request retransmission of an I frame that would be retransmitted by the REJ operation.) Likewise, a REJ frame is not transmitted if one or more earlier SREJ exception conditions have not been cleared as indicated in Section 4.5.4.

I frames transmitted following the I frame indicated by the SREJ frame are not retransmitted as the result of receiving a SREJ frame. Additional I frames awaiting initial transmission may be transmitted following the retransmission of the specific I frame requested by the SREJ frame.

4.3.3. Unnumbered Frame Control Fields

Unnumbered frame control fields are either commands or responses.

Figure 4.4 shows the layout of U frames implemented within this protocol.

Control Field Type		Type	Control-Field Bits			
			7 6 5	4	3 2	1 0
Set Async Balanced Mode	SABME	Cmd	0 1 1	P	1 1	1 1
Set Async Balanced Mode	SABM	Cmd	0 0 1	P	1 1	1 1
Disconnect	DISC	Cmd	0 1 0	P	0 0	1 1
Disconnect Mode	DM	Res	0 0 0	F	1 1	1 1
Unnumbered Acknowledge	UA	Res	0 1 1	F	0 0	1 1
Frame Reject	FRMR	Res	1 0 0	F	0 1	1 1
Unnumbered Information	UI	Either	0 0 0	P/F	0 0	1 1
Exchange Identification	XID	Either	1 0 1	P/F	1 1	1 1
Test	TEST	Either	1 1 1	P/F	0 0	1 1

Figure 4.4. U frame control fields.

Where:

Acronym	Description of Frame Identifiers
SABM	Connect Request
SABME	Connect Request Extended (modulo 128)
DISC	Disconnect request
FRMR	Frame Reject
UI	Unnumbered Information Frame
DM	Disconnect Mode - System Busy or Disconnected.
XID	Exchange Identifications - Negotiate features.
UA	Unnumbered Acknowledge
TEST	Test

4.3.3.1. Set Asynchronous Balanced Mode (SABM) Command

The SABM command places two Terminal Node Comtrollers (TNC) in the asynchronous balanced mode (modulo 8). This a balanced mode of operation in which both devices are treated as equals or peers.

Information fields are not allowed in SABM commands. Any outstanding I frames left when the SABM command is issued remain unacknowledged.

The TNC confirms reception and acceptance of a SABM command by sending a UA response frame at the earliest opportunity. If the TNC is not capable of accepting a SABM command, it responds with a DM frame if possible.

4.3.3.2. Set Asynchronous Balanced Mode Extended (SABME) Command

The SABME command places two TNCs in the asynchronous balanced mode extended (modulo 128). This is a balanced mode of operation in which both devices are treated as equals or peers.

Information fields are not allowed in SABME commands. Any outstanding I frames left when the SABME command is issued remains unacknowledged.

The TNC confirms reception and acceptance of a SABME command by sending a UA response frame at the earliest opportunity. If the TNC is not capable of accepting a SABME command, it responds with a DM frame. A TNC that uses a version of AX.25 prior to v2.2 responds with a FRMR.

4.3.3.3. Disconnect (DISC) Command

The DISC command terminates a link session between two stations. An information field is not permitted in a DISC command frame.

Prior to acting on the DISC frame, the receiving TNC confirms acceptance of the DISC by issuing a UA response frame at its earliest opportunity. The TNC sending the DISC enters the disconnected state when it receives the UA response.

Any unacknowledged I frames left when this command is acted upon remain unacknowledged.

4.3.3.4. Unnumbered Acknowledge (UA) Response

The UA response frame acknowledges the reception and acceptance of a SABM(E) or DISC command frame. A received command is not actually processed until the UA response frame is sent. Information fields are not permitted in a UA frame.

4.3.3.5. Disconnected Mode (DM) Response

The disconnected mode response is sent whenever a TNC receives a frame other than a SABM(E) or UI frame while in a disconnected mode. The disconnected mode response also indicates that the TNC cannot accept a connection at the moment. The DM response does not have an information field.

Whenever a SABM(E) frame is received and it is determined that a connection is not possible, a DM frame is sent. This indicates that the called station cannot accept a connection at that time.

While a TNC is in the disconnected mode, it responds to any command other than a SABM(E) or UI frame with a DM response with the P/F bit set to "1".

4.3.3.6. Unnumbered Information (UI) Frame

The Unnumbered Information frame contains PID and information fields and passes information along the link outside the normal information controls. This allows information fields to be exchanged on the link, bypassing flow control.

Because these frames cannot be acknowledged, if one such frame is obliterated, it cannot be recovered.

A received UI frame with the P bit set causes a response to be transmitted. This response is a DM frame when in the disconnected state, or an RR (or RNR, if appropriate) frame in the information transfer state.

4.3.3.7. Exchange Identification (XID) Frame

The Exchange Identification frame causes the addressed station to identify itself, and to provide its characteristics to the sending station. An information field is optional within the XID frame. A station receiving an XID command returns an XID response unless a UA response to a mode setting command is awaiting transmission, or a FRMR condition exists.

The XID frame complies with ISO 8885. Only those fields applicable to AX.25 are described. All other fields are set to an appropriate value. This implementation is compatible with any implementation which follows ISO 8885. Only the general-purpose XID information field identifier is required in this version of AX.25.

The information field consists of zero or more information elements. The information elements start with a Format Identifier (FI) octet. The second octet is the Group Identifier (GI). The third and forth octets form the Group Length (GL). The rest of the information field contains parameter fields.

The FI takes the value 82 hex for the general-purpose XID information. The GI takes the value 80 hex for the parameter-negotiation identifier. The GL indicates the length of the associated parameter field. This length is expressed as a two-octet binary number representing the length of the associated parameter field in octets. The high-order bits of length value are in the first of the two octets. A group length of zero indicates the lack of an associated parameter field and that all parameters assume their default values. The GL does not include its own length or the length of the GI.

The parameter field contains a series of Parameter Identifier (PI), Parameter Length (PL), and Parameter Value (PV) set structures, in that order. Each PI identifies a parameter and is one octet in length. Each PL indicates the length of the associated PV in octets, and is one octet in length. Each PV contains the parameter value and is PL octets in length. The PL does not include its own length or the length of its associated PI. A PL value of zero indicates that the associated PV is absent; the parameter assumes the default value. A PI/PL/PV set may be omitted if it is not required to convey information, or if present values for the parameter are to be used. The PI/PL/PV fields are placed into the information field of the XID frame in ascending order. There is only one entry for each PI/PL/PV field used. A parameter field containing an unrecognized PI is ignored. An omitted parameter field assumes the currently negotiated value.

The parameter fields described below represent the minimum implementation and do not preclude the negotiation of other parameters between consenting stations.

The encoding of each PI/PL/PV applicable to AX.25 is detailed in Figure 4.5. Some of the fields are defined in this standard. Only the fields discussed below are required in an implementation that complies with this version of AX.25.

Name	PI	PL	Parameter Field Element		Type	Bit	Value
Classes of Procedures	2	2	Balanced-ABM		E	1	1
			Unbalanced-NRM-Pri	*	E	2	0
			Unbalanced-NRM-Sec	*	E	3	0
			Unbalanced-ARM-Pri	*	E	4	0
			Unbalanced-ARM-Sec	*	E	5	0
			Half Duplex		E	6	0/1
			Full Duplex		E	7	0/1
			Reserved	*		8-16	0
HDLC Optional Functions	3	3	1 Reserved	*	E	1	0
			2 REJ cmd/resp		E	2	0/1
			3A SREJ cmd/resp		E	3	0/1
			4 UI cmd/resp	*	E	4	0
			5 SIM cmd/RIM resp	*	E	5	0
			6 UP cmd	*	E	6	0
			7A Basic address	*	E	7	0
			7B Extended address		E	8	1
			8 Delete I resp	*	E	9	0
			9 Delete I cmd	*	E	10	0
			10A Modulo 8		E	11	0/1
			10B Modulo 128		E	12	0/1
			11 RSET cmd	*	E	13	0
			12 TEST cmd/resp		E	14	1
			13 RD resp	*	E	15	0
			14A 16-bit FCS		E	16	1
			14B 32-bit FCS	*	E	17	0
			15A Synchronous Tx		E	18	1
			15B Start/stop Tx	*	E	19	0
			15C Start/Stop Basic Flow Ctl	*	E	20	0
			15D Start/stop Octet Transparent	*	E	21	0
			3B SREJ Multiframe	*	E	22	0
			Reserved	*	E	23-24	0
I Field Length Tx	5	N	Max I field length Tx (bits) N1*8	*	B	NA	B
I Field Length Rx	6	N	Max I field length Rx (bits) N1*8		B	NA	B
Window Size Tx	7	1	Window Size k (frames) TX	*	B B	1-7 8	0-127 0
Window Size Rx	8	1	Window Size k (frames) RX		B B	1-7 8	0-127 0
Ack Timer	9	N	Wait for Ack T1 (Msec)		B	NA	B
Retrys	10	N	Retry Count N2		B	NA	B

Figure 4.5. Parameter negotiation - parameter field elements.

- Note that Type E is a bit field and Type B is a numeric field of N octets.
- Parameter field elements marked * are defined in ISO 8885. They are shown for compatibility purposes only and are not needed to negotiate the features of this version of AX.25.

The Classes of Procedures parameter field (PI=2) serves to negotiate half- or full-duplex:

• Bit 1 is always a 1.
• Bits 2 through 5 and 8 through 16 are always zero.
• Either Bit 6 (half-duplex) or bit 7 (full-duplex), but not both, must be set. If this parameter field is not present, the current values are retained. The default is half-duplex.

The HDLC Optional Functions parameter field (PI=3) allows the negotiation of implicit reject (REJ), selective reject (SREJ), or selective reject-reject (SREJ/REJ) and modulo 8 or 128:

• Bits 1, 4-7, 9, 10, 13, 15, 17 and 19-24 are always zero.
• Bits 8, 14, 16 and 18 are always a one.
• Implicit reject is selected by setting bit 1 and resetting bit 2.
• Selective reject is selected by resetting bit 1 and setting bit 2.
• Selective reject-reject is selected by setting bit 1 and bit 2.
• Clearing both bit 1 and 2 is not allowed.
• Modulo 8 operation is selected by setting bit 11 and resetting bit 12.
• Modulo 128 operation is selected by setting bit 12 and resetting bit 11. If this parameter field is not present, the current values are retained. The default is selective reject-reject and modulo 8.

The I Field Length Receive parameter field (PI=6) allows the sending TNC to notify the receiving TNC of the maximum size of an Information field (N1) it will handle without error. A transmitting TNC may not exceed this size, but may send smaller frames. If this field is not present, the current values are retained. The default is 256 octets (2048 bits).

The Window Size Receive parameter field (PI=8) allows the sending TNC to notify the receiving TNC of the maximum size of the window (k) it will handle without error. If the TNCs are using modulo 128, this allows the negotiation of a window size less than 127 to conserve memory. If the TNCs are using selective reject or selective reject-reject, the receiving TNC is required to buffer k frames at any time. A transmitting TNC may not exceed this size, but may send fewer frames. If this field is not present, the current values are retained. The default is 4 for modulo 8 and 32 for modulo 128.

The Acknowledge Timer parameter field (PI=9) allows the negotiation of the wait for acknowledgement timer (T1). If this field is not present, the current values are retained. The default is 3000 MSec.

The Retries parameter field (PI=10) allows the negotiation of the retry count (N1). If this field is not present, the current values are retained. The default is 10 retries.

A FRMR condition may be established if the received XID command information field exceeds the maximum defined storage capability of the station, or if the receiving station is using AX.25 version 2.0 or earlier versions.

A typical XID frame is shown in Figure 4.6.

Flag	7E	Start Flag
A1	98	
A2	94	
A3	6E	
A4	A0	From Address (Example Call-SSID: NJ7P-0)
A5	40	
A6	40	
A7	E0	
A8	98	
A9	6E	
A10	98	
A11	8A	To Address (Example Call-SSID: N7LEM-0)
A12	9A	
A13	40	
A14	61	
Ctl	AF	Control Field (XID)
FI	82	Format indicator
GI	80	Group Identifier - parameter negotiation
GL	00	Group length - all of the PI/PL/PV fields
	17	(2 bytes)
PI	02	Parameter Indicator - classes of procedures
PL	02	Parameter Length
PV	00	Parameter Variable - Half Duplex, Async
	20	Balanced Mode
PI	03	Parameter Indicator - optional functions
PL	03	Parameter Length
PV	86	Parameter Variable - SREJ/REJ, extended addr
	A8	16-bit FCS, TEST cmd/resp, Modulo 128
	02	synchronous transmit
PI	06	Parameter Indicator - Rx I field length (bits)
PL	02	Parameter Length
PV	04	Parameter Variable - 1024 bits (128 octets)
	00	
PI	08	Parameter Indicator - Rx window size
PL	01	Parameter length
PV	02	Parameter Variable - 2 frames
PI	09	Parameter Indicator - Timer T1
PL	02	Parameter Length
PV	10	Parameter Variable - 4096 MSec
	00	
PI	0A	Parameter Indicator - Retries (N1)
PL	01	Parameter Length
PV	03	Parameter Variable - 3 retries
FCS	XX	
FCS	XX	
Flag	7E	

Figure 4.6. Typical XID frame.

4.3.3.8. Test (TEST) Frame

The Test command causes the addressed station to respond with the TEST response at the first respond opportunity; this performs a basic test of the data-link control. An information field is optional with the TEST command. If present, the received information field is returned, if possible, by the addressed station, with the TEST response. The TEST command has no effect on the mode or sequence variables maintained by the station.

A FRMR condition may be established if the received TEST command information field exceeds the maximum defined storage capability of the station. If a FRMR response is not returned for this condition, a TEST response without an information field is returned.

The station considers the data-link layer test terminated on receipt of the TEST response, or when a time-out period has expired. The results of the TEST command/response exchange are made available for interrogation by a higher layer.

4.3.3.9. FRMR Response Frame

The FRMR response is removed from the standard for the following reasons:

a) UI frame transmission was not allowed during FRMR recovery;
 b) During FRMR recovery, the link could not be reestablished by the station that sent the FRMR;
c) The above functions are better handled by simply resetting the link with a SABM(E) + UA exchange;
d) An implementation that receives and process FRMRs but does not transmit them is compatible with older versions of the standard;
and e) SDL is simplified and removes the need for one state.

This version of AX.25 operates with previous versions of AX.25. It does not generate a FRMR Response frame, but handles error conditions by resetting the link.

4.4. Link Error Reporting and Recovery

Several link-layer errors can be recovered without terminating the connection. These error situations may occur as a result of transmission errors or malfunctions within the TNC.

4.4.1. TNC Busy Condition

When a TNC is temporarily unable to receive I frames (e.g., when receive buffers are full), it sends a Receive Not Ready (RNR) frame. This informs the sending TNC that the receiving TNC cannot handle any more I frames at the moment. This receiving TNC clears this condition by the sending a UA, RR, REJ or SABM(E) command frame.

4.4.2. Send Sequence Number Error

If the send sequence number, N(S), of an otherwise error-free received frame does not match the receive state variable, V(R), a send sequence error has occurred. If SREJ has been negotiated and the N(s) is in the range "greater-than V(r)" and "less-than V(r)+k," the information field is saved; otherwise it is discarded. The receiver will not acknowledge this frame or any other I frames until N(S) matches V(R).

The control field of the erroneous I frame(s) is accepted so that link supervisory functions such as checking the P/F bit can be performed. Because of this update, the retransmitted I frame may have an updated P bit and N(R).

4.4.3. Reject (REJ) Recovery

The REJ frame requests a retransmission of I frames following the detection of a N(S) sequence error. Only one outstanding "sent REJ" condition is allowed at a time. This condition is cleared when the requested I frame has been received.

A TNC receiving the REJ command clears the condition by resending all outstanding I frames (up to the window size), starting with the frame indicated in N(R) of the REJ frame.

4.4.4. Selective Reject (SREJ) Recovery

The SREJ command/response initiates more-efficient error recovery by requesting the retransmission of a single I frame following the detection of a sequence error. This is an advancement over the earlier versions in which the requested I frame was retransmitted togther with all additional I frames subsequently transmitted and successfully received.

When a TNC sends one or more SREJ commands, each with the P bit set to "0" or "1", or one or more SREJ responses, each with the F bit set to "0", and the "sent SREJ" conditions are not cleared when the TNC is ready to issue the next response frame with the F bit set to "1", the TNC sends a SREJ response with the F bit set to "1", with the same N(R) as the oldest unresolved SREJ frame.

Because an I or S format frame with the F bit set to "1" can cause checkpoint retransmission, a TNC does not send SREJ frames until it receives at least one in-sequence I frame, or it perceives by timeout that the checkpoint retransmission will not be initiated at the remote TNC.

With respect to each direction of transmission on the data link, one or more "sent SREJ" exception conditions from a TNC to another TNC may be established at a time. A "sent SREJ" exception condition is cleared when the requested I frame is received.

The SREJ frame may be repeated when a TNC perceives by timeout that a requested I frame will not be received, because either the requested I frame or the SREJ frame was in error or lost.

When appropriate, a TNC receiving one or more SREJ frames initiates retransmission of the individual I frames indicated by the N(R) contained in each SREJ frame. After having retransmitted the above frames, new I frames are transmitted later if they become available.

When a TNC receives and acts on one or more SREJ commands, each with the P bit set to "0", or an SREJ command with the P bit set to "1", or one or more SREJ responses each with the F bit set to "0", it disables any action on the next SREJ response frame if that SREJ frame has the F bit set to "1" and has the same N(R) (i.e., the same value and the same numbering cycle) as a previously actioned SREJ frame, and if the resultant retransmission was made following the transmission of the P bit set to a "1".

When the SREJ mechanism is used, the receiving station retains correctly-received I frames and delivers them to the higher layer in sequence number order.

4.4.5. Timeout Error Recovery

4.4.5.1. T1 Timer Recovery

If a transmission error causes a TNC to fail to receive (or to receive and discard) a single I frame, or the last I frame in a sequence of I frames, then the TNC does not detect a send-sequence-number error and consequently does not transmit a REJ/SREJ. The TNC that transmitted the unacknowledged I frame(s) following the completion of timeout period T1, takes appropriate recovery action to determine when I frame retransmission as described in Section 6.4.10 should begin. This condition is cleared by the reception of an acknowledgement for the sent frame(s), or by the link being reset.

4.4.5.2. Timer T3 Recovery

Timer T3 ensures that the link is still functional during periods of low information transfer. When T1 is not running (no outstanding I frames), T3 periodically causes the TNC to poll the other TNC of a link. When T3 times out, an RR or RNR frame is transmitted as a command with the P bit set, and then T1 is started. When a response to this command is received, T1 is stopped and T3 is started. If T1 expires before a response is received, then the waiting acknowledgement procedure (Section 6.4.11) is executed.

4.4.6. Invalid Frame or FCS Error

If an invalid frame is received, or a frame is received with an FCS error, that frame is discarded with no further action taken.

5. Elements for Layer-to-Layer Communication

Communication between layers is accomplished with primitives. In an abstract way, primitives represent the logical exchange of information and control between the data link and adjacent layers; they do not specify or constrain implementations.

Primitives consist of commands and their respective responses associated with the services requested from a lower layer. The general syntax of a primitive is:

XXX - Generic name - Type: Parameters

Where "XXX" designates the interface across which the primitive flows.

For this Standard, "XXX" is:

a) DL for communications between Layer 3 and the data-link layer;
b) LM for communications between the data-link layer and the link multiplexer;
c) PH for communications between the link multiplexer and the physical layer; and
d) MDL for communications between Layer 3 and the layer management.

5.1. Layer 3 Entity <—> Management Data-link State Machine

Communication between the Layer 3 Entity and the Management Data-link State Machine is characterized by three primitives:

- **MDL-NEGOTIATE Request**. The Layer 3 entity uses this primitive to request the Data-link State Machine to notify/negotiate.

- **MDL-NEGOTIATE Confirm**. The Management Data-link State Machine uses this primitive to notify the Layer 3 entity that notification/negotiation is complete.

- **MDL-ERROR Indicate**. The Management Data-link State Machine uses this primitive to notify the Layer 3 entity that notification/negotiation has failed.

5.2. Management Data-Link State Machine <—> Link Multiplexer State Machine

Communication between the Management Data-link State Machine and the Link Multiplexer State Machine is characterized by two primitives:

- **LM-DATA Request**. The Management Data-link State Machine uses this primitive to pass frames of any type (XID, UI, etc.) to the Link Multiplexer State Machine.

- **LM-DATA Indication**. The Link Multiplexer State Machine uses this primitive to pass frames of any type (XID, UI, etc.)to the Management Data-link State Machine.

5.3. Layer 3 Entity <—> Data-Link State Machine

Communication between the Layer 3 Entity and the Data-link State Machine is characterized by thirteen primitives:

- **DL-CONNECT Request**. The Layer 3 entity uses this primitive to request the establishment of a AX.25 connection.

- **DL-CONNECT Indication**. The Data-link State Machine uses this primitive to indicate that a AX.25 connection has been requested.

- **DL-CONNECT Confirm**. The Data-link State Machine uses this primitive to indicate that a AX.25 connection has been made.

- **DL-DISCONNECT Request**. The Layer 3 entity uses this primitive to request the release of a AX.25 connection.

- **DL-DISCONNECT Indication**. The Data-link State Machine uses this primitive to indicate that a AX.25 connection has been released.

- **DL-DISCONNECT Confirm**. The Data-link State Machine uses this primitive to indicate that a AX.25 connection has been released and confirmed.

- **DL-DATA Request**. The Layer 3 entity uses this primitive to request the transmission of data using connection-oriented protocol. If necessary, this frame is examined and acted upon by the segmenter.

- **DL-DATA Indication**. The reassembler uses this primitive to indicate reception of Layer 3 data using connection oriented protocol.

- **DL-UNIT-DATA Request**. The Layer 3 entity uses this primitive to request the transmission of data using connectionless protocol. If necessary, this frame is examined and acted upon by the segmenter.

- **DL-UNIT-DATA Indication**. The reassembler uses this primitive to indicate reception of Layer 3 data using connectionless protocol.

- **DL-ERROR Indication**. The Data-link State Machine uses this primitive to indicate when frames inconsistent with this protocol definition have been received. This includes short frames, frames with inconsistent parameter values, etc. The error indications are discussed in the SDL appendices.

- **DL-FLOW-OFF Request**. The Layer 3 entity uses this primitive to temporarily suspend the flow of incoming information.

- **DL-FLOW-ON Request**. The Layer 3 entity uses this primitive to resume the flow of incoming information.

5.4. Data-Link State Machine <—> Link Multiplexer State Machine

Communication between the Data-link State Machine and the Link Multiplexer State Machine is characterized by six primitives:

- **LM-SEIZE Request**. The Data-link State Machine uses this primitive to request the Link Multiplexer State Machine to arrange for transmission at the next available opportunity. The Data-link State Machine uses this primitive when an acknowledgement must be made; the exact frame in which the acknowledgement is sent will be chosen when the actual time for transmission arrives.

- **LM-SEIZE Confirm**. This primitive indicates to the Data-link State Machine that the transmission opportunity has arrived.

- **LM-RELEASE Request**. The Link Multiplexer State Machine uses this primitive to stop transmission.

- **LM-EXPEDITED-DATA Request**. The data-link machine uses this primitive to pass expedited data to the link multiplexer.

- **LM-DATA Request**. The Data-link State Machine uses this primitive to pass frames of any type (SABM, RR, UI, etc.) to the Link Multiplexer State Machine.

- **LM-DATA Indication**. The Link Multiplexer State Machine uses this primitive to pass frames of any type (SABM, RR, UI, etc.) to the Data-link State Machine.

5.5. Link Multiplexer State Machine <—> Physical State Machine

Communication between the Link Multiplexer State Machine and the Physical State Machine is characterized by eight primitives:

- **PH-SEIZE Request**. The Link Multiplexer State Machine uses this primitive before each transmission to request access to the radio channel.

- **PH-SEIZE Confirm**. The Physical State Machine uses this primitive to confirm that the channel has been seized.

- **PH-RELEASE Request**. The Link Multiplexer State Machine uses this primitive to release the radio channel.

- **PH-QUIET Indication**. The Physical State Machine uses this primitive to indicate that the channel is not busy.

- **PH-BUSY Indication**. The Physical State Machine uses this primitive to indicate that the channel is busy.

- **PH-EXPEDITED-DATA Request**. The Link Multiplexer State Machine uses this primitive to request transmission of each digipeat or expedite data frame.

- **PH-DATA Request**. The Link Multiplexer State Machine uses this primitive to request transmission of each normal frame.

- **PH-DATA Indication**. The Physical State Machine uses this primitive to provide incoming frames to the link multiplexer.

5.6. Physical State Machine <—> Hardware

Communication between the Physical State Machine and the Hardware is characterized by five primitives:

- **Acquisition of Signal**. The hardware uses this primitive to notify the Physical State Machine that modem synchronization, flag fill or frame structure have been detected.

- **Loss of Signal**. The hardware uses this primitive to notify the Physical State Machine that modem synchronization, flag fill or frame structure have been lost.

- **Frame**. The hardware uses this primitive and the Physical State Machine to pass frames to send or that have been received.

- **Turn On Transmitter**. The Physical State Machine uses this primitive to tell the hardware to key the transmitter.

- **Turn Off Transmitter**. The Physical State Machine uses this primitive to tell the hardware to unkey the transmitter.

6. Description of AX.25 Procedures

The following paragraphs describe the procedures involved in setting up, using and disconnecting a balanced link between two TNC stations.

6.1. Address Field Operation

6.1.1. Address Information

All transmitted frames have address fields conforming to Section 3.12. All frames have both the destination device and the source device addresses in the address field, with the destination address coming first. This allows many links to share the same RF channel. The destination address is always the address of the station(s) for which the frame is intended; the source address contains the address of the device that sent the frame.

If point-to-multipoint operation is desired, the destination address can be a group name or club callsign. Operation with destination addresses other than actual amateur callsigns is a subject for further study.

6.1.2. Command/Response Procedure

AX.25 implements the command/response information in the address field. The command/response information is conveyed using two bits to maintain compatibility with previous versions of AX.25.

An upward-compatible AX.25 TNC communicating with a distant TNC determines if the latter is using an older version of this protocol by testing the command/response bit information located in bit 7 of the SSID octets of both the destination and source address subfields. If both C bits are set to "0", then the distant device is using the older protocol. The newer version of the protocol always has one of these two bits set to "1" and the other bit set to "0", depending on whether the frame is a command or a response.

The command/response information is encoded into the address field as shown in Figure 6.1. Implementations of AX.25 prior to version 2.0 defined these bits to be either both "0" or both "1".

Frame TypeDest.	SSID C-Bit	Source SSID C-Bit
Previous versions	0	0
Command (V.2.X)	1	0
Response (V.2.X)	0	1
Previous versions	1	1

Figure 6.1. Command/Response encoding.

Because all frames are considered to be either commands or responses, a device always has one of the bits set to "1" and the other bit set to "0".

The use of the command/response information in AX.25 allows S frames to be either commands or responses. This arrangement helps maintain proper control over the link during the information transfer state.

6.2. Poll/Final (P/F) Bit Procedures

The response frame returned by a TNC depends on the previous command received, as described in the following paragraphs.

The next response frame returned by the TNC to a SABM(E) or DISC command with the P bit set to "1" is a UA or DM response with the F bit set to "1".

The next response frame returned to an I frame with the P bit set to "1", received during the information transfer state, is an RR, RNR or REJ response with the F bit set to "1".

The next response frame returned to a supervisory command frame with the P bit set to "1", received during the information transfer state, is an RR, RNR or REJ response frame with the F bit set to "1".

The next response frame returned to a S or I command frame with the P bit set to "1", received in the disconnected state, is a DM response frame with the F bit set to "1".

The P bit is used in conjunction with the timeout recovery condition discussed in Section 4.5.5.

When not used, the P/F bit is set to "0".

6.3. Procedures For Link Set-Up and Disconnection

6.3.1. AX.25 Link Connection Establishment

To connect to a distant TNC, the originating TNC sends a SABM command frame to the distant TNC and starts its T1 timer. If the distant TNC exists and accepts the connect request, it responds with a UA response frame and resets all of its internal state variables (V(S), V(A) and V(R)). Reception of the UA response frame by the originating TNC causes it to cancel the T1 timer and set its internal state variables to "0".

If the distant TNC doesn't respond before T1 times out, the originating TNC resends the SABM frame and starts T1 running again. The originating TNC tries to establish a connection until it has tried unsuccessfully N2 times. N2 is defined in Section 6.7.2.3.

If the distant TNC receives a SABM command and cannot enter the indicated state, it sends a DM frame.

When the originating TNC receives a DM response to its SABM(E) frame, it cancels its T1 timer and does not enter the information-transfer state.

The originating TNC sending a SABM(E) command ignores and discards any frames except SABM, DISC, UA and DM frames from the distant TNC.

In response to a received SABM(E), frames other than UA and DM are sent only after the link is set up and if no outstanding SABM(E) exists.

6.3.2. Parameter Negotiation Phase

Parameter negotiation occurs at any time. It is accomplished by sending the XID command frame and receiving the XID response frame. Implementations of AX.25 prior to version 2.2 respond to an XID command frame with a FRMR response frame. The TNC receiving the FRMR uses a default set of parameters compatible with previous versions of AX.25.

The receipt of an XID response from the other station establishes that both stations are using AX.25 version 2.2 or higher and enables the use of the segmenter/reassembler and selective reject.

This version of AX.25 implements the negotiation or notification of six AX.25 parameters. Notification simply tells the distant TNC some limit that cannot be exceeded. The distant TNC can choose to use the limit or some other value that is within the limits. Notification is used with the Window Size Receive (k) and Information Field Length Receive (N1) parameters. Negotiation involves both TNCs choosing a value that is mutually acceptable. The XID command frame contains a set of values acceptable to the originating TNC. The distant TNC chooses to accept the values offered, or other acceptable values, and places these values in the XID response. Both TNCs set themselves up based on the values used in the XID response. Negotiation is used by Classes of Procedures, HDLC Optional Functions, Acknowledge Timer and Retries.

The Classes of Procedure parameter field (PI=2) negotiates half- or full-duplex operation. This reverts to half-duplex if either TNC cannot support full-duplex (i.e., if the XID command requests full-duplex and the receiving TNC can only support half-duplex, it sets the value to half-duplex in the XID response. If this parameter field is not present, the default half-duplex operation is selected.

The HDLC Optional Functions parameter field (PI=3) allows the negotiation of implicit reject (REJ), selective reject (SREJ), or selective reject-reject (SREJ/REJ), and modulo 8 or 128. Function reverts to the lesser of the selection offered in the XID command and XID response frames. Ordering is (highest to lowest): selective reject-reject, selective reject and implicit reject: Modulo 128 and modulo 8. If this parameter field is absent, the default function selective reject and modulo 8 are selected.

The I Field Length Receive parameter field (PI=6) allows the sending TNC to notify the receiving TNC of the maximum size of an Information field (N1) it will handle without error. A transmitting TNC may not exceed this size, but may send smaller frames.

The Window Size Receive parameter field (PI=8) allows the sending TNC to notify the receiving TNC of the maximum size of the window (k) it will handle without error. If the TNCs are using modulo 128, this allows the negotiation of a window size less than 127 to conserve memory. If the TNCs are using selective reject or selective reject-reject, the receiving TNC is required to buffer k frames at any time.

The Acknowledge Timer parameter field (PI=9) allows the negotiation of the "Wait for Acknowledgement" timer (T1). Function reverts to the greater of the values offered in the XID command and XID response frames.

The Retries parameter field (PI=10) allows the negotiation of the retry count (N1). Function reverts to the greater of the values offered in the XID command and XID response frames.

Defaults for the negotiated parameters for use with a previous version of AX.25 are:

Set Half Duplex
Set Implicit Reject
Modulo = 8
I Field Length Receive = 2048 bits
Window Size Receive = 4
Acknowledge Timer = 3000 MSec
Retries = 10

Defaults for the negotiated parameters for use with this version of AX.25 are:

Set Half Duplex
Set Selective Reject
Modulo = 8
I Field Length Receive = 2048 bits
Window Size Receive = 7
Acknowledge Timer = 3000 MSec
Retries = 10

6.3.3. Information-Transfer Phase

After establishing a link connection, the TNC enters the information-transfer state. In this state, the TNC accepts and transmits I and S frames according to the procedure outlined in Section 6.4.

If the TNC receives a SABM(E) command while in the information-transfer state, it follows the resetting procedure outlined in Section 6.5.

6.3.4. Link Disconnection

While in the information-transfer state, either TNC may indicate a request to disconnect the link by transmitting a DISC command frame and starting timer T1.

After receiving a valid DISC command, the TNC sends a UA response frame and enters the disconnected state. After receiving a UA or DM response to a sent DISC command, the TNC cancels timer T1 and enters the disconnected state.

If a UA or DM response is not correctly received before T1 times out, the DISC frame is sent again and T1 is restarted. If this happens N2 times, the TNC enters the disconnected state.

6.3.5. Disconnected State

In the disconnected state, a TNC monitors received commands, reacts to the receipt of a SABM(E) as described in Section 6.3.1, and transmits a DM frame in response to a DISC command.

In the disconnected state, a TNC may initiate a link set up as outlined in connection establishment (Section 6.3.1). It may also respond to the receipt of a SABM(E) command and establish a connection, or it may refuse the SABM(E) and send a DM instead.

Any TNC receiving a command frame other than a SABM(E) or UI frame with the P bit set to "1" responds with a DM frame with the F bit set to "1". The offending frame is ignored.

When the TNC enters the disconnected state after an error condition, or if an internal error has resulted in the TNC being in the disconnected state, the TNC indicates this by sending a DM response rather than a DISC frame and follows the link disconnection procedure outlined in Section 6.3.4. The TNC may then try to reestablish the link using the link set up procedure outlined in Section 6.3.1.

6.3.6. Collision Recovery

6.3.6.1. Collisions in a Half-Duplex Environment

Collisions of frames in a half-duplex environment are taken care of by the retry nature of the T1 timer and retransmission count variable. No other special action is required.

6.3.6.2. Collisions of Unnumbered Commands.

If sent and received SABM(E) or DISC command frames are the same, both TNCs send a UA response at the earliest opportunity, and both devices enter the indicated state.

If sent and received SABM(E) or DISC commands are different, both TNCs enter the disconnected state and transmit a DM frame at the earliest opportunity.

6.3.6.3. Collision of a DM with a SABM(E) or DISC

When an unsolicited DM response frame is sent, a collision between it and a SABM(E) or DISC may occur. In order to prevent this DM from being misinterpreted, all unsolicited DM frames are transmitted with the F bit set to "0". All SABM(E) and DISC frames are sent with the P bit set to "1". This prevents confusion when a DM frame is received.

6.3.7. Connectionless Operation

An additional type of operation exists in amateur radio that is not feasible using Layer 2 connections. This is the "round-table" operation, in which several amateurs may be engaged in one conversation. This type of operation cannot be accommodated by current AX.25 link-layer connections.

The way round-table activity is implemented is technically outside the AX.25 connection, although it still uses the AX.25 frame structure.

AX.25 uses a special frame for this operation, the Unnumbered Information (UI) frame. In this type of operation, the destination address has a code word installed in it that prevents users of that specific round-table from seeing all frames going through the shared RF medium. For example, if a group of amateurs are engaged in a round-table discussion about packet radio, they could put "PACKET" in the destination address; they will receive frames only from others in the same discussion. An added advantage of the use of AX.25 in this manner is that the source of each frame is in the source address subfield; software could be written to automatically display who is making what comments.

Since this mode is connectionless, there are no requests for retransmissions of bad frames. Without the handshaking activity of a point-to-point connection, collisions may also occur, with the potential of losing the frames that collided.

6.4. Procedures for Information Transfer

Once a connection has been established as outlined above, both TNCs can accept I, S and U frames.

6.4.1. Sending I Frames

Whenever a TNC has an I frame to transmit, it sends the I frame with the N(S) of the control field equal to its current send state variable V(S). After the I frame is sent, the send state variable is incremented by one. If timer T1 is not running, it is started. If timer T1 is running, it is restarted.

The TNC does not transmit any more I frames if its send state variable equals the last received N(R) from the other side of the link plus k. If the TNC sent more I frames, the flow control window would be exceeded and errors could result.

If a TNC is in a busy condition, it may still send I frames as long as the distant TNC is not also busy.

6.4.2. Receiving I Frames

The reception of I frames that contain zero-length information fields is reported to the next layer; no information field will be transferred.

6.4.2.1. Not Busy

If a TNC receives a valid I frame (one with a correct FCS and whose send sequence number equals the receiver's receive state variable) and is not in the busy condition, it accepts the received I frame, increments its receive state variable, and acts in one of the following manners:

a) If it has an I frame to send, that I frame may be sent with the transmitted N(R) equal to its receive state variable V(R) (thus acknowledging the received frame). Alternately, the TNC may send an RR frame with N(R) equal to V(R), and then send the I frame.

or b) If there are no outstanding I frames, the receiving TNC sends an RR frame with N(R) equal to V(R). The receiving TNC may wait a small period of time before sending the RR frame to be sure additional I frames are not being transmitted.

6.4.2.2. Busy

If the TNC is in a busy condition, it ignores any received I frames without reporting this condition, other than repeating the indication of the busy condition.

If a busy condition exists, the TNC receiving the busy condition indication polls the sending TNC periodically until the busy condition disappears.

A TNC may poll the busy TNC periodically with RR or RNR frames with the P bit set to "1".

6.4.3. Priority Acknowledge

This version of AX.25 implements the priority acknowledgement procedure. This feature precludes a non-priority frame from being transmitted during slot 0, the time when the TNC receiving the previous frame would be expected to send an acknowledgement.

6.4.4. Reception of Out-of-Sequence Frames

6.4.4.1. Implicit Reject (REJ)

When an I frame is received with a correct FCS but its send sequence number N(S) does not match the current receiver's receive state variable, the frame is discarded. A REJ frame is sent with a receive sequence number equal to one higher than the last correctly received I frame if an uncleared N(S) sequence error condition has not been previously established. The received state variable and poll bit of the discarded frame is checked and acted upon, if necessary.

This mode requires no frame queueing and frame resequencing at the receiver. However, because the mode requires transmission of frames that may not be in error, its throughput is not as high as selective reject. This mode is ineffective on systems with long round-trip delays and high data rates.

6.4.4.2. Selective Reject (SREJ)

When an I frame is received with a correct FCS but its send sequence number N(S) does not match the current receiver's receive state variable, the frame is retained. SREJ frames are sent with a receive sequence number equal to the value N(R) of the missing frame, and P=1 if an uncleared SREJ condition has not been previously established. If an SREJ condition is already pending, an SREJ will be sent with P=0. The received state variable and poll bit of the received frame are checked and acted upon, if necessary.

This mode requires frame queueing and frame resequencing at the receiver. The holding of frames can consume precious buffer space, especially if the user device has limited memory available and several active links are operational.

6.4.4.3. Selective Reject-Reject (SREJ/REJ)

When an I frame is received with a correct FCS but its send sequence number N(S) does not match the current receiver's receive state variable, and if N(S) indicates 2 or more frames are missing, a REJ frame is transmitted. All subsequently received frames are discarded until the lost frame is correctly received. If only one frame is missing, a SREJ frame is sent with a receive sequence number equal to the value N(R) of the missing frame. The received state variable and poll bit of the received frame are checked and acted upon. If another frame error occurs prior to recovery of the SREJ condition, the receiver saves all frames received after the first errored frame and discards frames received after the second errored frame until the first errored frame is recovered. Then, a REJ is issued to recover the second errored frame and all subsequent discarded frames.

6.4.5. Reception of Incorrect Frames

When a TNC receives a frame with an incorrect FCS, an invalid frame, or a frame with an improper address, that frame is discarded.

6.4.6. Receiving Acknowledgement

Whenever an I or S frame is correctly received, even in a busy condition, the N(R) of the received frame is checked to see if it includes an acknowledgement of outstanding sent I frames. The T1 timer is canceled if the received frame actually acknowledges previously unacknowledged frames. If the T1 timer is canceled and there are still some frames that have been sent that are not acknowledged, T1 is started again. If the T1 timer expires before an acknowledgement is received, the TNC proceeds with the retransmission procedure outlined in Section 6.4.11.

6.4.7. Receiving REJ

After receiving a REJ frame, the transmitting TNC sets its send state variable to the same value as the REJ frame's received sequence number in the control field. The TNC then retransmits any I frame(s) outstanding at the next available opportunity in accordance with the following:

a) If the TNC is not transmitting at the time and the channel is open, the TNC may begin retransmission of the I frame(s) immediately.

b) If the TNC is operating on a full-duplex channel transmitting a UI or S frame when it receives a REJ frame, it may finish sending the UI or S frame and then retransmit the I frame(s).

c) If the TNC is operating in a full-duplex channel transmitting another I frame when it receives a REJ frame, it may abort the I frame it was sending and start retransmission of the requested I frames immediately.

d) The TNC may send just the one I frame outstanding, or it may send more than the one indicated if more I frames followed the first unacknowledged frame, provided that the total to be sent does not exceed the flow-control window (k frames).

If the TNC receives a REJ frame with the poll bit set, it responds with either an RR or RNR frame with the final bit set before retransmitting the outstanding I frame(s).

6.4.8. Receiving an SREJ

After receiving a SREJ frame, the transmitting TNC retransmits the individual I frame indicated by the N(R) contained in the SREJ at the next available opportunity. After retransmitting the frame above, new I frames may be retransmitted subsequently if they become available. If the P bit was set, then all frames up to N(R)-1 are acknowledged.

6.4.9. Receiving an RNR Frame

Whenever a TNC receives an RNR frame, it stops transmitting I frames until the busy condition is cleared. If timer T3 expires after the RNR was received, an RR or RNR command with the P bit set is sent to poll the distant TNC of its status; then timer T1 is started. If an RNR frame is received in response to this poll, T1 is stopped and T3 is started again. If no response is received before T1 expires, the waiting acknowledgment procedure (Section 6.4.11) is performed. If an RR frame is received in response to the poll, then T1 is stopped and the busy condition cleared.

6.4.10. Sending a Busy Indication

Whenever a TNC enters a busy condition, it indicates this by sending an RNR response at the next opportunity. While the TNC is in the busy condition, it may receive and process S frames. If a received S frame has the P bit set to "1", the TNC sends an RNR frame with the F bit set to "1" at the next possible opportunity. To clear the busy condition, the TNC sends either an RR or REJ frame with the received sequence number equal to the current receive state variable, depending on whether the last received I frame was properly received or not.

6.4.11. Waiting Acknowledgement

If the originating TNC's timer T1 expires while awaiting the distant TNC's acknowledgement of an I frame transmitted, the originating TNC restarts timer T1 and transmits an appropriate supervisory command frame (RR or RNR) with the P bit set.

If the TNC correctly receives a supervisory response frame with the F bit set and with an $N(R)$ within the range from the last $N(R)$ received to the last $N(S)$ sent plus one, the TNC restarts timer T1 and sets its send state variable $V(S)$ to the received $N(R)$. It may then resume with I frame transmission or retransmission, as appropriate.

If, on the other hand, the TNC correctly receives a supervisory response frame with the F bit not set, or an I frame or supervisory command frame, and with an $N(R)$ within the range from the last $N(R)$ received to the last $N(S)$ sent plus one, the TNC does not restart timer T1; it uses the received $N(R)$ as an indication of acknowledgement of transmitted I frames up to and including I frame numbered $N(R)-1$.

If timer T1 expires before a supervisory response frame with the F bit set is received, the TNC retransmits an appropriate supervisory command frame (RR or RNR) with the P bit set. After N2 attempts to get a supervisory response frame with the F bit set from the distant TNC, the originating TNC initiates a link resetting procedure as described in Section 6.5.

6.5. Resetting Procedure

The link resetting procedure initializes both directions of data flow after a unrecoverable error has occurred. This resetting procedure is used only in the information-transfer state of an AX.25 link.

A TNC initiates a reset procedure whenever it receives an unexpected UA response frame, or after receipt of a FRMR frame from a TNC using an older version of the protocol.

A TNC resets the link by sending a SABM(E) frame and starting timer T1. After receiving a SABM(E) frame from the TNC to which it was previously connected, the receiver of a SABM(E) frame sends a UA frame back at the earliest opportunity, sets its send and receive state variables $V(S)$ and $V(R)$ to "0" and stops T1, unless it has sent a SABM(E) or DISC itself. If the UA frame is correctly received by the first TNC, it resets its send and receive state variables $V(S)$ and $V(R)$, and stops timer T1. Any busy condition that previously existed is also cleared.

If a DM response is received, the TNC enters the disconnected state and stops timer T1. If timer T1 expires before a UA or DM response frame is received, the SABM(E) is retransmitted and timer T1 restarted. If timer T1 expires N2 times, the TNC enters the disconnected state. Any previously existing link conditions are cleared.

Other commands or responses received by the TNC before completion of the reset procedure are discarded.

One TNC may request that the other TNC reset the link by sending a DM response frame. After the DM frame is sent, the sending TNC then enters the disconnected state.

6.6. Disassembler/Reassembler

The segmenter/reassembler procedure is only enabled if both stations on the link are using AX.25 version 2.2 or higher. The use of the segmenter/reassembler allows the transmission of packets longer than N1 in a simple and clean manner. This adds less than one percent overhead for the standard N1 of 256 bytes. It also adds the ability to send large Level 3 data entities such as IP datagrams as single entities over AX.25.

The segmenter is a simple process that divides long data units into smaller segments for transmission, attaching a two-octet header to each segment. At the receiving end, segments are reassembled into the original data unit. Overhead is kept to a minimum throughout; steps are taken to prevent deadlock situations from arising in the buffer management of both stations on the link. The header is illustrated in Figure 6.2.

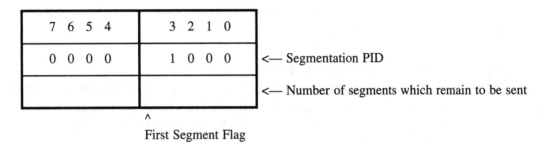

Figure 6.2 Segment header format.

The reassembler can tell when a segmented frame is received by the PID. If the first segment flag is set, then the amount of buffer space required for the entire frame can be calculated and allocated. If using the segmenter over connectionless service and a segment is lost, error recovery is not done by the reassembler. An error is passed to Layer 3; it is up to Layer 3 to recover.

6.7. List of System Defined Parameters

6.7.1. Timers

Thirteen timers maintain the integrity of the AX.25 Layer 2 connection and are discussed in the following subsections.

6.7.1.1. Acknowledgment Timer T1

T1, the Acknowledgement Timer, ensures that a TNC does not wait indefinitely for a response to a frame it sends. This timer cannot be expressed in absolute time; the time required to send frames varies greatly with the signaling rate used at Layer 1. T1 should take at least twice the amount of time it would take to send maximum length frame to the distant TNC and get the proper response frame back from the distant TNC. This allows time for the distant TNC to do some processing before responding.

If Layer 2 repeaters are used, the value of T1 should be adjusted according to the number of repeaters through which the frame is being transferred.

6.7.1.2. Response Delay Timer T2

T2, the Response Delay Timer, may optionally be implemented by the TNC to specify a maximum amount of delay to be introduced between the time an I frame is received and the time the resulting response frame is sent. This delay is introduced to allow a receiving TNC to wait a short period of time to determine if more than one frame is being sent to it. If more frames are received, the TNC can acknowledge them at once (up to seven), rather than acknowledging each individual frame. The use of timer T2 is not required; it is simply recommended to improve channel efficiency. Note that to achieve maximum throughput on full-duplex channels, acknowledgments should not be delayed beyond k/2 frames. The k parameter is defined in Section 6.8.2.3.

6.7.1.3. Inactive Link Timer T3

T3, the Inactive Link Timer, maintains link integrity whenever T1 is not running. It is recommended that whenever there are no outstanding unacknowledged I frames or P-bit frames (during the information-transfer state), an RR or RNR frame with the P bit set to "1" be sent every T3 time units to query the status of the other TNC. The period of T3 is locally defined, and depends greatly on Layer 1 operation. T3 should be greater than T1; it may be very large on channels of high integrity.

6.7.1.4. Repeater Hang Timer T100 (AXHANG)

T100, the Repeater Hang Timer, tracks the amount of time an audio repeater will keep its transmitter keyed after it stops receiving. This timer can increase channel efficiency when an audio repeater is used. If the repeater's transmitter remains keyed, it is not necessary to add AXDELAY to the transmitter key-up time.

6.7.1.5. Priority Window Timer T101 (PRIACK)

T101, the Priority Window Timer, prevents stations from transmitting non-priority frames during the first available transmission time slot. The first transmission time slot is reserved for priority frames (acknowledgments and digipeat frames).

6.7.1.6. Slot Time Timer T102 (p-persistence)

T102, the Slot Time Timer, randomly delays stations before they begin transmitting immediately after the channel becomes clear. This helps prevent several stations from beginning to transmit at the same time and causing collisions.

6.7.1.7. Transmitter Startup Timer T103 (TXDELAY)

T103, the Transmitter Startup Timer, allows time to be reasonably certain that the transmitter has properly ramped up and is ready to transmit after being keyed, before any frames are sent.

6.7.1.8. Repeater Startup Timer T104 (AXDELAY)

T104, the Repeater Startup Timer, allows time to be reasonably certain that audio repeaters have had time to start their transmitters before frames are sent.

6.7.1.9. Remote Receiver Sync Timer T105

T105, the Remote Receiver Sync Timer, introduces additional delay time after TXDELAY, if needed, to allow a remote receiver to sync up before transmitting frames.

6.7.1.10. Ten Minute Transmission Limit Timer T106

T106, the Ten Minute Transmission Limit Timer, ensures that the transmitter is not keyed for more than ten minutes.

6.7.1.11. Anti-Hogging Limit Timer T107

T107, the Anti-Hogging Limit Timer, prevents a station from monopolizing the channel.

6.7.1.12. Receiver Startup Timer T108

T108, the Receiver Startup Timer, allows sufficient time to be reasonably certain that the receiver is monitoring the status of the channel (busy or not) after unkeying the transmitter, before attempting to start transmitting again.

6.7.1.13. Next Segment Timer TR210

T210, the Next Segment Timer, ensures that the reassembler doesn't wait forever for the next segment of a segmented frame.

6.7.2. Parameters

6.7.2.1. Maximum Number of Octets in an I Field (N1)

The default maximum number of octets allowed in the I field is 256. This variable is negotiable between end stations. The I field is an integral number of octets.

6.7.2.2. Maximum Number of Retries (N2)

The maximum number of retries is used in conjunction with the T1 timer.

6.7.2.3. Maximum Number of I Frames Outstanding (k)

The maximum number of I frames outstanding at a time is seven (modulo 8) or 127 (modulo 128).

APPENDIX B

D-STAR System

Technical Requirements for the Wireless System

1.1   Voice Communication

1.1.1   General Terms

(1) Communication Method
   Half-duplex, digitized voice transmissions.
(2) Communication Contents
   Digitized voice/audio signals and short data messages are supported. Voice and audio streams are transmitted synchronously to support communications quality reproduction. Data and voice/audio transmissions are interleaved.

1.1.2   Transmitting Equipment

(1) Modulation methods
   GMSK
   QPSK
   4FSK
(2) Data rate
   Maximum of 4.8 Kbps
(3) Voice encoding method
   AMBE (2020) converting at 2.4 Kbps
   FEC at 3.6 Kbps
(4) Occupied bandwidth
   Maximum of 6 KHz

1.1.3   Tx / Rx Switching time
   Less than 100ms.

1.2   Data Communication

1.2.1   General Terms
   (1) Communication Method
      Simplex
   (2) Communication Contents
      Digital data stream is supported.

1.2.2 Transmitting Equipment

    (1) Modulation method
       GMSK
       QPSK
       4FSK
    (2) Data rate
       Maximum of 128 Kbps

    (3) Occupied bandwidth
       Maximum of 150 KHz

1.1.3 Switching time (Tx-Rx)
Less than 50ms.

1.3 Backbone communication

1.3.1 General Terms
    (1) Transmission Method
       Full duplex.
    (2) Transmission Contents
       Backbone communication between repeaters containing multiplexed digitized voice/audio, user data, and link control data signals.

1.3.2 Transmitting Setup
    (1) Output power
       Complies with FCC regulations.
    (2) Modulation method
       GMSK
    (3) Data rate
       Maximum of 10Mbps
    (5) Occupied bandwidth
       Maximum of 10.5MHz

1.3.3 Multiplexing Method
The multiplexing method for backbone links is an ATM. The details of the specifications comply with the ATM protocol. Digitized voice/audio signals should be given the highest transmission priority.

If more data is required, refer to ATM standards.

ATM Cell (53byte) →

| Header | □□□□□□□ | Header | □□□□□□□ | Header | □□□□□□□ |

5byte   48byte

2. System Interconnection Requirements

2.1 Wireless Communication Packet

The frame structure of the wireless packet is below.

2.1.1 Frame structure of a data packet

Radio Header												Data					FCS
					ID								MAC Header			Data frame	
Bit Syn	Frame Syn.	Flag 1	Flag 2	Flag 3	Destina-tion Repeater Callsign	Depart-ure Repeater Callsign	Compa-nion Callsign	Own Callsign 1	Own Callsign 2	P_FCS	E_Len	SA	DA	Type			CRC
64bit	15bit	1	1 byte	1	8byte	8byte	8byte	8byte	4byte		2byte	2byte	6byte	6byte	2byte	6-1500byte	4byte

|←——————— error correction   660bit ——————→|

The explanation of the data frame structure the Radio Header follows.

(1) **Bit Syn**. (Bit synchronization): Repeated standard 64-bit synchronization pattern (for GMSK 1010, for QPSK 1001). Transmission direction is from left to right.

(2) **Frame Syn**. (Frame synchronization) : 15bit pattern (111011001010000). Transmission direction is from left to right.

(3) **Flag 1** (8 bit):   Flag 1 uses upper 5 bits and lower 3 bits separately.
    A detailed explanation follows.

bit 7(MSB)	Distinguishes between voice and data communications. 1 indicates data, 0 indicates voice.
bit 6	Identifies if the signal goes through a repeater or is a direct communication between terminals.(1for repeater, 0 for terminal)
bit 5	Recognizes if communication interruption exists. 1 indicates interruption, 0 indicates no interruption.
bit 4	Identifies control signal/data signal.1 represents control signal and 0 represents regular data signal.(Voice signal included)
bit 3	1 represents an urgent priority signal,0 represents a normal priority signal.

For signals with a "1" in this position, the receiver will open squelch etc.

> Note, Urgent signal in this document does not mean "Urgency signal" as defined in International Radio Law. It means an urgent priority signal for use in emergency communications.

bit 2,1,0	111=repeater station control flag, while the repeater is controlled, the flag is "111" and the data frame contains control data.

        110=Auto reply

        101=Unused(spare)

        100=Resend flag, requests resending previous frame

        011=ACK flag,Treated as ACK flag

        010=No reply flag, Indicates no reply is available

        001=Relay unavailable flag, Indicates unsuitable relaying conditions.

        000=NULL, No information.

Bit	Upper bit				
	7	6	5	4	3
1	Data	Relay	Interruption	Control	Urgent
0	Voice	Direct	No interruption	Control	Urgent

Lower bit				
2	1	0	Function	Note
1	1	1	Repeater Control	Repeater Control Mode
1	1	0	Auto Reply	Used for Auto Reply
1	0	1	(Unused)	(Unused0
1	0	0	Resend	Requests Resend
0	1	1	ACK	ACK flag
0	1	0	No Response	Indicates No Response Available
0	0	1	Relay Unavailable	Indicates Relay Unavailable
0	0	0	NULL	NULL

(4) Flag 2

Flag 2 is for future expandability and is defined below.

Bit	7	6	5	4	3	2	1	0	Note
Flag									
									Default

a.   flag is used as an format descriptor. This is available not only for the increase and decrease of a figure of callsign but also for ID, which is not used as callsign rather than numeric.

b.   flag is used only a creator or a manufacturer of the equipment.

(5) Flag 3

Flag 3 is used to match control functions to protocol versions, which may be upgraded in future software versions.

Bit	Meaning	Function
00000000	No	Default

	Function	
00000001		
to	Undefined	Use for future expansion
11111111		

(6) "**Destination repeater Callsign**" can have a maximum of 8 ASCII letters and numbers. Blanks should be filled with a space character. In the case of direct communication, it inserts "   " and fills the blanks with a space character. The use of this field is described in section 2.2.

(7) "**Departure repeater Callsign**" can have a maximum of 8 ASCII letters and numbers. Blanks should be filled with a space character. In the case of direct communication, it inserts "   " and fills the blanks with a space character. The use of this field is described in section 2.2.

(8) "**Companion Callsign**" can have a maximum of 8 ASCII letters and numbers. Blanks should be filled with a space character. The use of this field is described in section 2.2.

(9) "**Own Callsign 1**" can have a maximum of 8 ASCII letters and numbers. Blanks should be filled with a space character. This field same as voice frames.

(10) "**Own Callsign 2**" is used when to add suffixes to a callsign or an additional destination address information. "Own Callsign 2" can have a maximum of 4 ASCII letters and numbers. Blanks should be filled with a space character.

(11) **P_FCS** is the Radio Header CRC-CCITT checksum, computed by the following expression.
$$G(x) = x^{16} + x^{12} + x^5 + 1$$

(12) The **data frame** of the packet is constructed as an Ethernet packet.

(13) **FCS** is the checksum of the Ethernet data payload. It is a CRC-32 checksum as defined in ISO3309 and is computed by the following expression.
$$G(x) = x^{32} + x^{26} + x^{23} + x^{22} + x^{16} + x^{12} + x^{11} + x^{10} + x^8 + x^7 + x^5 + x^4 + x^2 + x + 1$$

2.1.2 Frame structure of voice packet

Radio Header										Data						
					ID											
Bit Syn	Frame Syn.	Flag 1	Flag 2	Flag 3	Destination Repeater Callsign	Departure Repeater Callsign	Compa-nion Callsign	Own Callsign 1	Own Callsign 2	P_FCS	Voice Frame	Data Frame	Voice Frame	Data Frame	Voice Frame	Data Frame
64bit	15bit	1	1	1	8byte	8byte	8byte	8byte	4byte	2byte	72byt	24byte	72byte	24byte	72byte	24byt

|←—byte——— error correction 660bit ————————→|

The explanation of the voice packet including the voice and data frames follows:

(1) The Radio Header has the same frame structure as for the data packet.

(2) Data part includes 72-bit voice signal frames with a length of 20ms in order of their output from the CODEC according to the AMBE (w/FEC) specification. Data frames contain 24-bits of data.

(3) The first data frame and then every 21st data frame in a repeating cycle, are used only for synchronizing data for each modulation type. Synchronization corrects for the lag between transmission and reception, including the transit time of communications. This synchronized signal contains a 10-bit synchronized signals and two 7-bit Maximal-length sequences "1101000" patterns. (24 bits total). Transmission direction is from left to right.

(4) The data in a data frame is transmitted without modification from the input data. If the data is required as error correction or synchronization, these frames are processed before processing the data input.

(5) If the data signal length is greater than the length of the voice communication the transmitting switch is turned on until the completion of the data signal manually. The processing can be allowed automatically.

(6) The last data frame, which requires a means of terminating the transmission, is a unique synchronizing signal (32 bit + 15bit "000100110101111" + "0", making 48 bits) as defined by the modulation type. Transmission direction is from left to right.

2.2   Communication protocol

Note : In the following descriptions,_ (under-bar) indicates a space character, ASCII $20. If the callsign field has blanks between the callsign's last letter and last character in the field, the blanks should be filled with a space character.

2.2.1 Callsign

The Callsign field of the radio header of data and voice packets is used for packet routing. Except for the callsign in the "Own station" fields, callsigns generally have less than 6 letters (or 7 letters). The following paragraphs show how to interpret callsign fields:.

(1) "**Destination repeater Callsign**"

In zone communication, this field must be set to the callsign of the repeater utilized by the companion station.

If there are multiple repeaters in a repeater site, they are distinguished by last character, of "A", "B", "C", or "D". (Ex. W$1AAA_A , W$1AAA_D, etc.) The default character is "A".

(Explained callsign is not to exist as W$1AAA but only for examples)

When communicating outside the local zone, which is called zone to zone communication, this field must be set to the callsign of the zone repeater connected to a gateway and last character set to "G" to indicate communications via the gateway. (Ex. W$1AAA_G)

(2) **"Departure repeater Callsign"**

This field must be set to the repeater callsign of the originating station.

If there are multiple repeaters in a repeater site, they are distinguished by last character of "A", "B", "C", or "D". (Ex. W$1AAA_A , W$1AAA_D etc.) The default character is "A".

(3) **"Companion Callsign"**

The field must be set the callsign of the companion station with which communication is desired. If the station has multiple radios,, they are distinguished by last character of "A", "B", "C", "D", "E", or "F". (Ex. W$1AAA_A , W$1AAA_F etc.)

When originating a non-directed call,, the field should contain "CQCQCQ".

When calling CQ to a non-local zone, which is called zone to zone communication, prepend "/" to the destination repeater callsign. If there are multiple repeaters in a repeater site, they are distinguished by last character of "A", "B", "C", or "D". (Ex. W$1AAA_A , W$1AAA_D etc.) The default character is "A".
To access a repeater with a local server, in "Companion Callsign", the field should contain the repeater callsign and set last character to "S". (Ex. W$1BBB_S)

(4) **"Own Callsign 1"**

The "Own Callsign" field contains the own station's callsign. If the station has multiple radios, they are distinguished by last character of "A", "B", "C", "D", "E", or "F". (Ex. W$1AAA_A , W$1AAA_F etc.)

(5) **"Own Callsign 2"**

This field contains information to display as in after a "/ (slash)". (Ex. W$1AAA_F / JD1 etc. Note: "/" is not displayed). The purpose of "Own Callsign 2" is to allow "Own Callsign 1" to contain as complete a callsign as possible. "Own Callsign 2" is not evaluated by the system's identification functions.

Appendix

AP1 Scrambler

Scrambling is implemented as follows to eliminate errors when the same bit patterns are received continuously.

AP1.1 Scramble codes

$$S(x) = x^7 + x^4 + 1$$

Initialization defines   . Initialization begins the scrambling process.

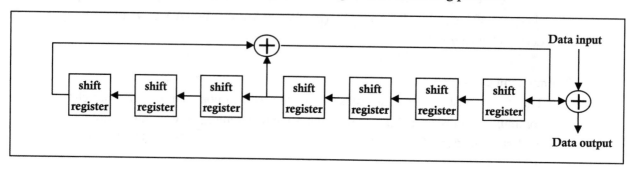

AP1.2 Data packet scrambling

Radio Header												Data					FCS
					ID								MAC Header				
Bit Syn	Frame Syn.	Flag 1	Flag 2	Flag 3	Destination Repeater Callsign	Departure Repeater Callsign	Companion Callsign	Own Callsign 1	Own Callsign 2	P_FCS	E_Len		SA	DA	Type	Data frame	CRC
64bit	15bit	1	1 byte	1	8byte	8byte	8byte	8byte	4byte		2byte	2byte	6byte	6byte	2byte	6-1500byte	4byte

|←————— error correction   660bit —————→|

Scramble range

↑ Initialization point

AP1.3 Voice packet scrambling

Voice packet scrambling includes the radio header and data frames except for synchronizing frames. Synchronized signals and the last frame are not scrambled.

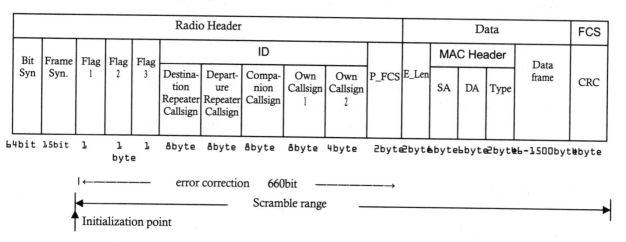

Radio Header											Data							
					ID													
Bit Syn	Frame Syn.	Flag 1	Flag 2	Flag 3	Destination Repeater Callsign	Departure Repeater Callsign	Companion Callsign	Own Callsign 1	Own Callsign 2	P_FCS	Voice Frame	Data Frame	Voice Frame	Data Frame		Voice Frame	Data Frame	
64bit	15bit	1	1	1	8byte	8byte	8byte	8byte	4byte	2byte	72byte	24byte	72byte	24byte		72byte	24byte	

|←————— error correction   660bit —————→|
scramble

| scram |

↑ Initialization Point   ↑ Initialization point

AP2 Error Correction

Error correction for data voice packets is performed as follows.

The error correction range is from Flag 1 to P-FCS.

The error correction signal is interleaved with the packet data with a convolutional rate of 1/2, a constraint length of 3, and a depth of interleave of 24.

The structure of encoder
    Convolution code
    Convolutional code rate   /
    Constraint length
    Handover bit
    Generator polynomial
    $G_1(D) = 1 + D + D^2$
    $G_2(D) = 1 + D^2$

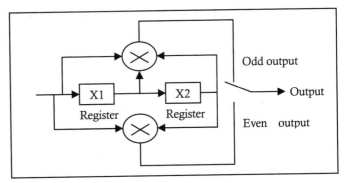

Composing process

(1) X1, X2 registers must be set to zero before encoding.

(2) Feed header data into the encoder beginning with the LSB.

(3) Following the header data, including P_FCS, input two zero bits.

AP3   Interleave process

To reduce continuous burst errors during the radio header, the interleaving process specified by the following interleave matrix is used. The interleave process operates independently of the error correction process.

    To interleave transmit error correction, input the packet data stream from left top to the bottom. Read the interleaved data stream from left top to right.

    To separate the error correction data and original data stream, input from the received data stream from the left top to right. Read the output data stream from the left top to the bottom.

interleave structure MATRIX

(ms)		0.2	0.4	0.6	0.8	1	1.2	1.5	1.7	1.9	2.1	2.3	2.5	2.7	2.9	3.1	3.3	3.5	3.7	4	4.2	4.4	4.6	4.8	5	5.2	5.4	5.6	5.8
		0	1	2	3	4	5	6	7	8	9	10	11	12	13	14	15	16	17	18	19	20	21	22	23	24	25	26	27
0.21	0	0	24	48	72	96	120	144	168	192	216	240	264	288	312	336	360	384	408	432	456	480	504	528	552	576	600	624	648
6.03	1	1	25	49	73	97	121	145	169	193	217	241	265	289	313	337	361	385	409	433	457	481	505	529	553	577	601	625	649
12.1	2	2	26	50	74	98	122	146	170	194	218	242	266	290	314	338	362	386	410	434	458	482	506	530	554	578	602	626	650
18.1	3	3	27	51	75	99	123	147	171	195	219	243	267	291	315	339	363	387	411	435	459	483	507	531	555	579	603	627	651
24.1	4	4	28	52	76	100	124	148	172	196	220	244	268	292	316	340	364	388	412	436	460	484	508	532	556	580	604	628	652
30.2	5	5	29	53	77	101	125	149	173	197	221	245	269	293	317	341	365	389	413	437	461	485	509	533	557	581	605	629	653
36.2	6	6	30	54	78	102	126	150	174	198	222	246	270	294	318	342	366	390	414	438	462	486	510	534	558	582	606	630	654
42.2	7	7	31	55	79	103	127	151	175	199	223	247	271	295	319	343	367	391	415	439	463	487	511	535	559	583	607	631	655
48.3	8	8	32	56	80	104	128	152	176	200	224	248	272	296	320	344	368	392	416	440	464	488	512	536	560	584	608	632	656
54.3	9	9	33	57	81	105	129	153	177	201	225	249	273	297	321	345	369	393	417	441	465	489	513	537	561	585	609	633	657
60.3	10	10	34	58	82	106	130	154	178	202	226	250	274	298	322	346	370	394	418	442	466	490	514	538	562	586	610	634	658
66.4	11	11	35	59	83	107	131	155	179	203	227	251	275	299	323	347	371	395	419	443	467	491	515	539	563	587	611	635	659
72.4	12	12	36	60	84	108	132	156	180	204	228	252	276	300	324	348	372	396	420	444	468	492	516	540	564	588	612	636	
75.7	13	13	37	61	85	109	133	157	181	205	229	253	277	301	325	349	373	397	421	445	469	493	517	541	565	589	613	637	
81.5	14	14	38	62	86	110	134	158	182	206	230	254	278	302	326	350	374	398	422	446	470	494	518	542	566	590	614	638	
87.4	15	15	39	63	87	111	135	159	183	207	231	255	279	303	327	351	375	399	423	447	471	495	519	543	567	591	615	639	
93.2	16	16	40	64	88	112	136	160	184	208	232	256	280	304	328	352	376	400	424	448	472	496	520	544	568	592	616	640	
99	17	17	41	65	89	113	137	161	185	209	233	257	281	305	329	353	377	401	425	449	473	497	521	545	569	593	617	641	
105	18	18	42	66	90	114	138	162	186	210	234	258	282	306	330	354	378	402	426	450	474	498	522	546	570	594	618	642	
111	19	19	43	67	91	115	139	163	187	211	235	259	283	307	331	355	379	403	427	451	475	499	523	547	571	595	619	643	
116	20	20	44	68	92	116	140	164	188	212	236	260	284	308	332	356	380	404	428	452	476	500	524	548	572	596	620	644	
122	21	21	45	69	93	117	141	165	189	213	237	261	285	309	333	357	381	405	429	453	477	501	525	549	573	597	621	645	
128	22	22	46	70	94	118	142	166	190	214	238	262	286	310	334	358	382	406	430	454	478	502	526	550	574	598	622	646	
134	23	23	47	71	95	119	143	167	191	215	239	263	287	311	335	359	383	407	431	455	479	503	527	551	575	599	623	647	

Lexicon

Gate way (GW)

Equipment of to connect between a zone repeater and the Internet. Usally it is normal PC including D-STAR GW softwares.

Zone

A region of connected multi repeaters by backbone repeaters.

Zone repeater

Connected a repeater to the Internet in a zone.

Repeater area

A region of available to access a repeater to the terminals.

Repeater site

A place of setting some repeaters and/or backbone repeaters.

Figure of System constitution

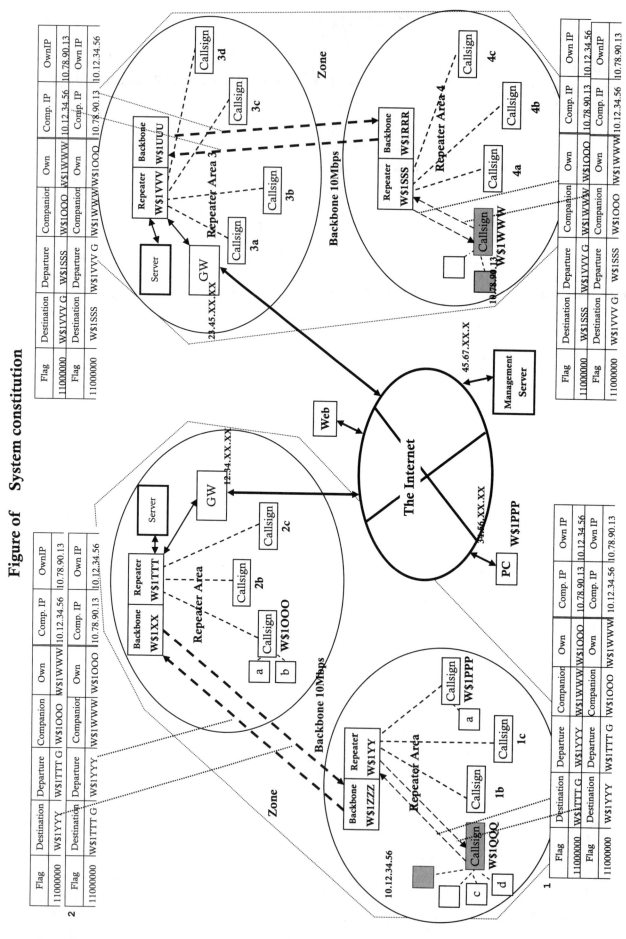

APPENDIX C

Reprinted with permission from Daniels Electronics from
P25 Radio Systems Training Guide

ANATOMY OF THE COMMON AIR INTERFACE

VOICE

The P25 standard requires the use of the IMBE™ Vocoder to encode speech (tone and audio level) into a digital bit stream. The IMBE™ digital bit stream is broken ino voice frames where each voice frame is 88 bits in length (representing 20 ms of speech). The voice frames are protected with error correction codes which add 56 parity check bits resulting in an overall voice frame size of 144 bits. The voice frames are grouped into Logical Link Data Units (LDU1 and LDU2) that contain 9 voice frames each. Each Logical Link Data Unit is 180 ms in length and can be consecutively grouped into Superframes of 360 ms. The superframes are repeated continuously throughout the voice message after a Header Data Unit has been sent. Additional information (encryption, Link Control information and Low Speed Data) is interleaved throughout the voice message.

The voice message structure for a P25 CAI voice transmission is shown in Figure 4-1. The voice message begins with a Header Data Unit (to properly initialize any encryption and link control functions for the message), and then continues with Logical Link Data Units or LDUs. The LDUs alternate until the end of the voice message. The end of the message is marked with a Terminator Data Unit. The Terminator Data Unit can follow any of the other voice data units.

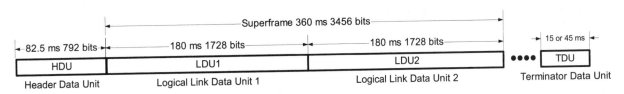

Figure 4-1: P25 Voice Message Structure

DATA

Data messages are transmitted over the P25 CAI using a packet technique. The data information is broken into fragments, packets and blocks are then error coded and sent as a single packet called a Packet Data Unit. The Packet Data Unit can be of varying lengths and includes a header block that contains the length of the data message.

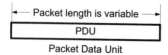

Packet Data Unit

Figure 4-2: P25 Data Message Structure

FRAME SYNCHRONIZATION AND NETWORK IDENTIFIER

Each data unit (Header Data Unit, Logical Link Data Unit 1, Logical Link Data Unit 2, Packet Data Unit and Terminator Data Unit) begins with a Frame Synchronization (FS) and Network Identifier (NID).

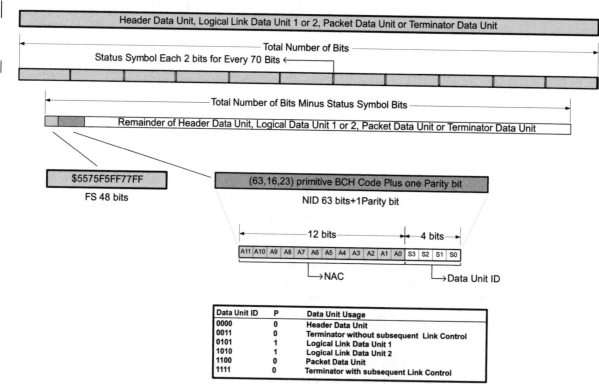

Data Unit ID	P	Data Unit Usage
0000	0	Header Data Unit
0011	0	Terminator without subsequent Link Control
0101	1	Logical Link Data Unit 1
1010	1	Logical Link Data Unit 2
1100	0	Packet Data Unit
1111	0	Terminator with subsequent Link Control

The codes for the 6 different data units are shown.
The other 10 data units not shown are reserved for use in trunking or other systems.
The P bit is the last (64-th) parity bit in the code word.

Figure 4-3: Frame Synchronization and Network Identifier

STATUS SYMBOLS

Throughout all of the data units (Header Data Unit, Logical Link Data Unit 1, Logical Link Data Unit 2, Packet Data Unit and Terminator Data Unit) the 2 bit status symbols are interleaved so that there is one status symbol for every 70 bits of information.

Status Symbol	Meaning	Usage
01	Inbound Channel is Busy	Repeater
00	Unknown, use for talk-around	Subscriber
10	Unknown, use for inbound or outbound	Repeater or Subscriber
11	Inbound Channel is Idle	Repeater

HEADER DATA UNIT

A diagram of the header data unit is given in Figure 4-4. The Header Data Unit is composed of the FS (48 bits), NID (64 bits), and the header code word (648 bits). Ten null bits are added to the end of the header code word resulting in 770 bits. Eleven status symbols are also interleaved throughout the Header Data Unit yielding 792 bits total. The Header Data Unit takes 82.5 ms to transmit at 9.6 kbps (the standard bit rate of the P25 CAI).

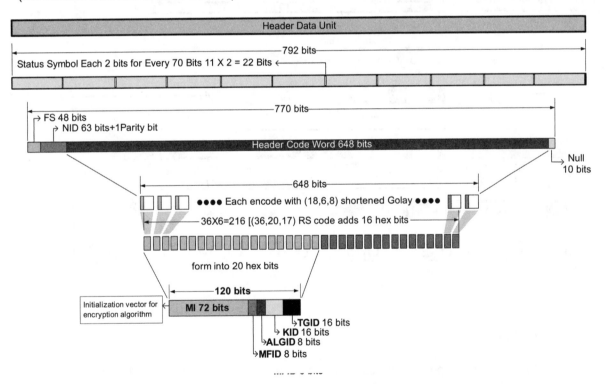

Figure 4-4: Header Data Unit

The Header Code Word field includes a **Message Indicator** (MI), and **Algorithm ID** (ALGID) for the encryption algorithm, and the **Key ID** (KID) for the encryption key as well as the **Manufacturer's ID** (MFID) and **Talk-group ID** (TGID). These information fields total 120 bits.

The information fields are separated into 20 symbols of 6 bits each (these are called hex bits). The symbols or hex bits are encoded with a (36,20,17) Reed-Solomon code to yield 36 hex bits. The 36 hex bits are then encoded with a (18,6,8) shortened Golay code to yield 648 bits total.

VOICE CODE WORDS

The IMBE™ vocoder converts speech into a digital bit stream where the bit stream is broken into voice frames of 88 bits in length for every 20 ms of speech. This corresponds to a continuous average vocoder bit rate of 4.4 kbps. Voice frames consist of 8 information vectors, labelled u_0, u_1, ... u_7.

Voice frames are encoded into a 144 bit voice code word as follows:

The voice frame bits are rated according to their effect on audio quality and are then protected using Golay and Hamming codes. The 48 most important bits (u_0 through u_3) are error protected with four (23,12,7) Golay code words. The next 33 most significant bits (u_4 through u_6) are error protected with three (15,11,3) Hamming code words. The last 7 least significant bits (u_7) are not error protected. Construction of the IMBE™digital bit stream into voice code words is given in Figure 4-5.

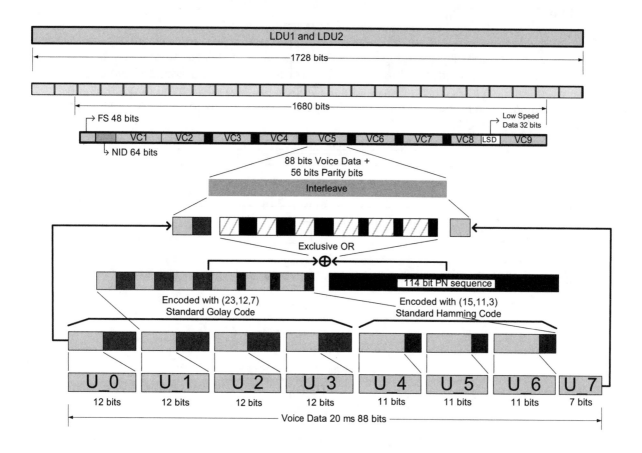

Figure 4-5: Voice Code Word

After the voice data has been error protected using the Golay and Hamming codes, a 114 bit pseudo random sequence (PN sequence) is generated from the 12 bits of u_0. The error protected voice data in u_1 through u_6 is then bit-wise exclusive-ored with the PN sequence. This information is then interleaved throughout the voice frame to resist fades.

LOGICAL LINK DATA UNIT 1

A diagram of Logical Link Data Unit 1 (LDU1) is given in Figure 4-6. LDU1 is the first half of a superframe. LDU1 is composed of the FS (48 bits), NID (64 bits), nine voice code words, numbered VC1 through VC9 (1296 bits), Link Control Word (240 bits) and Low Speed Data (32 bits). Twenty-Four Status Symbols are also interleaved throughout LDU1 yielding 1728 bits total. LDU1 takes 180 ms to transmit at 9.6 kbps (the standard bit rate of the P25 CAI).

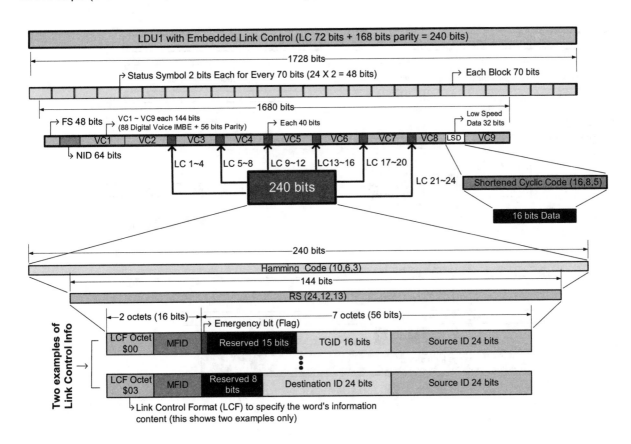

Figure 4-6: Logical Data Unit 1

The Link Control Word field may include a **Talk-group ID** (TGID), a **Source ID**, a **Destination ID**, an **Emergency** indicator, a **Manufacturer's ID** (MFID) and any other necessary call ID information. The Link Control Word uses a variable format since there is too much information for a fixed field format. The type of format is identified by the **Link Control Format** (LCF). The LCF specifies the the content of the Link Control Word's information. Two format examples are diagrammed in Figure 4-6. All of the information fields (including the LCF) total 72 bits.

The Link Control Word is constructed by serializing the information into 12 hex bits and then encoding them with a (24,12,13) RS code to yield 24 hex bits. The 24 hex bits are then encoded with a (10,6,3) shortened Hamming code to yield 240 bits total. The 240 bits of Link Control (LC) information is then inserted in between the voice code words (VC2 to VC8) in blocks of 40 bits (LC 1-4 is a block of 40 bits, etc.).

LOGICAL LINK DATA UNIT 2

A diagram of Logical Link Data Unit 2 (LDU2) is given in Figure 4-7. LDU2 is the second half of a superframe. LDU2 is composed of the FS (48 bits), NID (64 bits), nine voice code words, numbered VC10 through VC18 (1296 bits), Encryption Sync Word (240 bits) and Low Speed Data (32 bits). Twenty-Four Status Symbols are also interleaved throughout LDU1 yielding 1728 bits total. LDU2 takes 180 ms to transmit at 9.6 kbps (the standard bit rate of the P25 CAI).

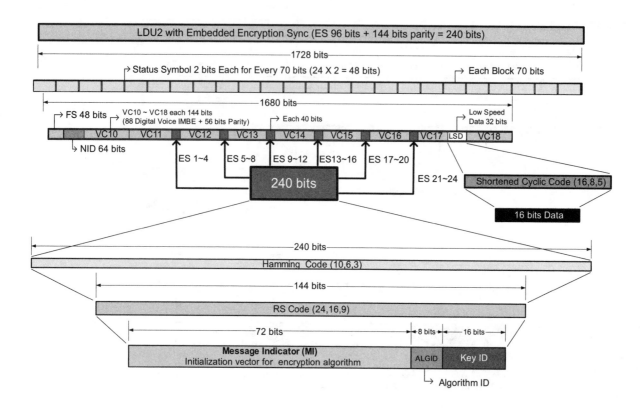

Figure 4-7: Logical Data Unit 2

The Encryption Sync Word field includes the **Message Indicator** (MI), **Algorithm ID** (ALGID) for the encryption algorithm, and the **Key ID** (KID) for the encryption key. This information may be used to support a multi-key encryption system, but is also used for single key and clear messages.

The Encryption Sync Word is constructed by serializing the information into 16 hex bits and then encoding them with a (24,16,9) RS code to yield 24 hex bits. The 24 hex bits are then encoded with a (10,6,3) shortened Hamming code to yield 240 bits total. The 240 bits of Encryption Sync (ES) information is then inserted in between the voice code words (VC11 to VC17) in blocks of 40 bits (ES 1-4 is a block of 40 bits, etc.).

LOW SPEED DATA

Low Speed Data is a serial stream of information. This information is provided for custom applications that are not defined in the CAI. Low Speed Data is comprised of 32 bits of data, 16 bits of which are inserted between VC8 and VC9 in LDU1 and 16 bits are inserted between VC17 and VC18 in LDU2. Each group of 16 bits is encoded with a (16,8,5) shortened cyclic code, creating 32 bits total in each LDU. Low Speed Data has a total capacity of 88.89 bps.

TERMINATOR DATA UNIT

Voice messages may use one of two different Terminator Data Units.. The simple Terminator Data Unit is composed of the FS (48 bits), NID (64 bits), and Null bits (28 bits). A diagram of the simple Terminator Data Unit is given in Figure 4-8.

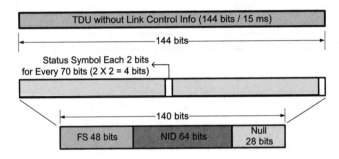

Figure 4-8: Terminator Data Unit without Link Control Info

The Terminator Data Unit can also be sent with the Link Control Word embedded in it. A diagram of the expanded Terminator Data Unit is given in Figure 4-9. The Link Control Word is the same as the Link Control Word used in LDU1, except that it is error protected with a Golay code instead of the Hamming code.

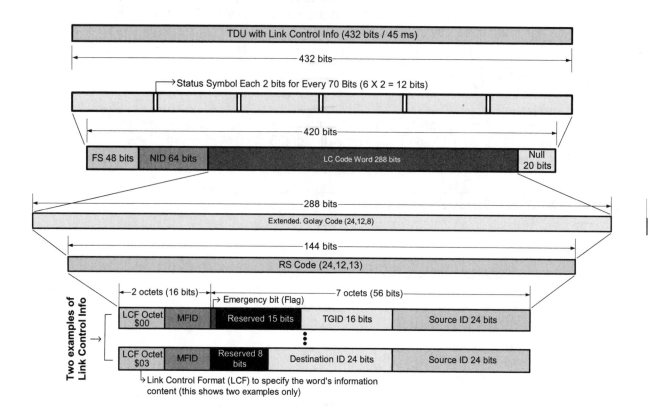

Figure 4-9: Terminator Data Unit with Link Control Info

When the voice message is finished, the transmitter continues the transmission, by encoding silence for the voice, until the Logical Link Data Unit is completed. Once the Logical Link Data Unit is completed, the transmitter then sends the Terminator Data Unit to signify the end of the message. The terminating data unit may follow either LDU1 or LDU2.

PACKET DATA UNIT

A diagram of the Packet Data Unit is given in Figure 4-10. Data Packets use two different types of data with two different structures. Confirmed or uncomfirmed delivery may be used to send data. Confirmed delivery is used when the recipient of the packet is required to send an acknowledgment of receipt. Unconfirmed delivery does not require an acknowledgment of receipt. Confirmed or unconfirmed delivery is defined in the header block.

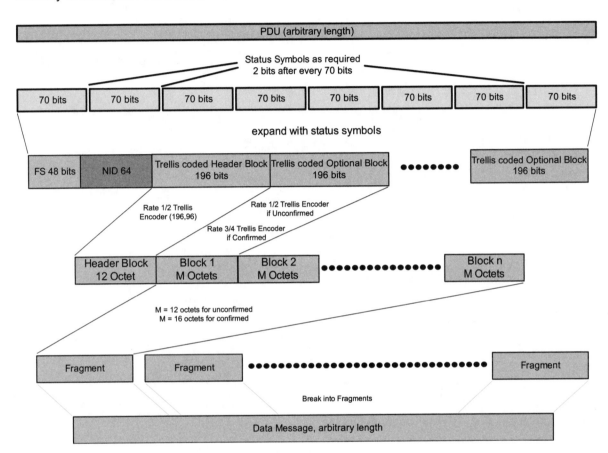

Figure 4-10: Data Packet Unit

Data is sent in variable length packets and the length of the data packet is defined in the header block. When a data packet ends, nulls are added until the next status symbol.

The data message is split into fragments, then formed into packets, and the packets are then split into a sequence of information blocks that are error protected by a Trellis code. These blocks are then transmitted as a single data packet.

INDEX

NOTES

NOTES

NOTES

FEEDBACK

Please use this form to give us your comments on this book and what you'd like to see in future editions, or e-mail us at **pubsfdbk@arrl.org** (publications feedback). If you use e-mail, please include your name, call, e-mail address and the book title, edition and printing in the body of your message. Also indicate whether or not you are an ARRL member.

Where did you purchase this book?
☐ From ARRL directly ☐ From an ARRL dealer

Is there a dealer who carries ARRL publications within:
☐ 5 miles ☐ 15 miles ☐ 30 miles of your location? ☐ Not sure.

License class:
☐ Novice ☐ Technician ☐ Technician Plus ☐ General ☐ Advanced ☐ Amateur Extra

Name _____

ARRL member? ☐ Yes ☐ No

Call Sign _____

Daytime Phone ( ) _____ Age _____

Address _____

City, State/Province, ZIP/Postal Code _____

If licensed, how long? _____ E-mail _____

Other hobbies _____

Occupation _____

For ARRL use only	VHF Dig
Edition	1 2 3 4 5 6 7 8 9 10 11 12
Printing	2 3 4 5 6 7 8 9 10 11 12

From _____

_____

_____

EDITOR, VHF DIGITAL HANDBOOK
AMERICAN RADIO RELAY LEAGUE
225 MAIN STREET
NEWINGTON CT 06111-1494

— — — — — — — — — — — — — please fold and tape — — — — — — — — — — — — —